The Magic Flute
(Die Zauberflöte)

Opera in two Acts by
Wolfgang Amadeus Mozart

Words by Carl Ludwig Giesecke
and Emanuel Schikaneder

English Version by Edward J. Dent

Vocal Score by Erwin Stein

Boosey & Hawkes
Music Publishers Limited
London · Paris · Bonn · Johannesburg · Sydney · Toronto · New York

Printed in England

10.95

THE story of *The Magic Flute* has often been regarded as a childish jumble of absurdities. The opera was planned as a spectacular fairy play with music for a popular theatre, but for some unknown reason the whole plot was altered at an early stage and the opera became an allegory of Freemasonry, which, largely under English influences, had spread all over Germany during the eighteenth century and was secretly disseminating ideals of English liberalism and humanitarianism. These ideals met with the determined hostility of the absolute monarchies and of the Roman Catholic Church, all the more so since in France they had led to the Revolution. Mozart was a devoted Freemason and so were many of the leading spirits of his time such as Goethe and Haydn; it has been alleged that Beethoven was a Freemason, too, and he was certainly associated with Freemasons and influenced by their doctrines. The libretto of *The Magic Flute* had been first suggested by an oriental fairy-tale in Wieland's *Dschinnistan*, but for the Masonic symbolism the main source of its episodes was *Sethos*, an edifying novel by the Abbé Terrasson, first published in Paris, 1731, and soon translated into both German and English; it was much read in Masonic circles. The scene of the opera is laid in ancient Egypt, and the Freemasons are represented by a college of priests headed by Sarastro; the name is obviously imitated from that of Zoroaster. Tamino, a young prince, is rescued from a gigantic serpent by three mysterious ladies who invite him to resue Pamina, the daughter of the Queen of Night, from Sarastro, whom they describe to him as a tyrant of monstrous cruelty. Tamino, led to the temple by three Genii, discovers to his surprise that Sarastro is the exact opposite of what he had been told. He decides to apply for initiation into the mysteries of the priests, and in the second act he submits to various tests of moral endurance. He meets Pamina for a moment at the end of Act I, but he is not allowed to speak to her until the final test of fire and water through which they pass together to the blessed company of the initiates. Pamina herself is also subjected to trials of a different kind, including the persecutions of her mother, the Queen of Night, and a grotesquely revolting negro, Monostatos, who has generally been supposed to symbolize the Church. Lastly, Tamino is accompanied throughout the opera by a comic figure, half man, half bird, Papageno, whose part in the play is that of a kind of Harlequin or Kasperle, the traditional idiotic servant of Viennese comedy. Schikaneder, actor-manager and part author, wrote this part for himself, and seized every opportunity for personal success. Mozart, however, was deeply impressed by the serious side of the story, and the scenes of mystery have a spiritual intensity paralleled only by the *Requiem* which he was composing at the same time and left unfinished at his death.

The Masonic symbolism of the opera has often been denied or minimized by writers unfriendly to Freemasonry, but it has been openly recognized both in Germany and in England from the first. J. R. Planché pointed it out when making his English version in 1838, and it is common knowledge that Freemasons of to-day acknowledge the significance of certain scenes and certain musical rhythms familiar in their ritual. Freemasons are naturally cautious and reserved when asked questions by outsiders; people who are not Freemasons and not even interested in the subject naturally prefer to ignore the allegory. Catholic writers are in duty bound to disapprove of it, although they dare not in this country make open attack on a society which is universally respected and honoured.

Certainly it is not necessary to be a Freemason to enter into the spirit of the opera. Tamino and Pamina stand for Everyman and Everywoman; their ceremonial trials symbolize the sufferings and experiences of a lifetime, the fire and water, the passions and sorrows of all humanity. The historic importance of *The Magic Flute* is that it was the first great masterpiece of music, perhaps the first of any art, that was deliberately created for what are called "the masses" and not for a restricted aristocracy. Beethoven, Spohr, Weber and Wagner recognized it as the foundation-stone of German opera; we may now receive it as one of the master-works that Germany has presented to the whole world.

Characters

Tamino, *an Egyptian Prince*	*Tenor*
Three Ladies *in attendance on the Queen of Night* ...	*Two Sopranos and Mezzosoprano*
Papageno, *a bird-catcher*	*Baritone (High Bass)*
The Queen of Night...	*Soprano*
Monostatos, *a Moor in the service of Sarastro* ...	*Tenor*
Pamina, *daughter of the Queen of Night*	*Soprano*
Three Genii	*Two Sopranos and Mezzosoprano*
The Orator...	*Bass*
Sarastro, *High Priest of Isis and Osiris*	*Bass*
Two Priests	*Tenor and Bass*
Papagena	*Soprano*
Two Men in Armour	*Tenor and Bass*

Slaves, Priests, People, etc.

The scene is laid in Egypt in the neighbourhood of a temple of Isis and Osiris

First performance, Vienna, 30*th September* 1791. *First performance in Paris (much distorted and mutilated as 'Les Mystères d'Isis'),* 20*th August* 1801. *First performances in London, King's Theatre,* 6*th June* 1811 *(in Italian); Covent Garden,* 27*th May* 1833 *(in German); Drury Lane,* 10*th March* 1838 *(in English). First performance in English, New York,* 17*th April* 1833. *First performance of this English version, New Theatre, Cambridge* 1*st December* 1911.

Index

In addition to the grace-notes which Mozart himself wrote down in the vocal parts it has been customary to sing many additional appoggiaturas, especially in recitatives, following the Italian convention which dates back to long before the days of Mozart. These appoggiaturas have not been printed in the present score because they have always been traditionally left to the discretion of the singers. No hard and fast rule can be laid down for their performance, but in most cases where a descending phrase has a feminine ending, i.e., with an accented penultimate syllable followed by a final syllable on a weak beat, both being given the same musical note, the strong beat should be treated as an appoggiatura and sung to the note one degree above that actually written, so that the cadence falls by a tone or semitone to the final note.

Examples:

p. 62

p. 63

THE MAGIC FLUTE

Overture

W. A. Mozart

Printed in England.

H. 15564

f
sf
sf
sf
p
f
sf
sf
sf
p
cresc.
f

Adagio
Allegro

sf
sf
sf
sf
sf
p
f
sf
sf

f
sf
sf
p
cresc.
f
Ped.
Ped.
Ped.
Ped.
ff
p
sf
sf
p
sf
sf
p
sf
sf
f

ACT I

Scene 1. A rocky scene, with trees and hills on either side.

No. 1 Introduction

Allegro
TAMINO rushes on, carrying a bow, but no arrows.
He is pursued by a huge serpent.
cresc.
TAMINO
Oh help me! pro-tect me! will no one stand
Zu Hül - fe! zu Hül - fe! sonst bin ich ver -
T.
by me? De-sert - ed in dan-ger, oh where shall I
- lo - ren! Zu Hül - fe! zu Hül - fe! sonst bin ich ver -

T.
fly me? The poi - son-ous fangs of the ser - pent are on me_ O
lo - ren, der li - sti-gen Schlan-ge zum O - pfer er - ko - ren! Barm-
gods, now have mer - cy! See, near - er it
- her - zi - ge Göt - ter! Schon na - het sie
draws With white cru - el jaws! Too
sich, schon na - het sie sich; ach
late it is, too late it is, I can - not fly_ Ye
ret - tet mich, ach ret - tet, ret - tet, schüt - zet mich, ach
THREE LADIES enter, carrying spears, and kill the serpent.
gods pro-tect me, or I die, pro-tect me, or I
schüt - zet, schüt - zet, ret - tet, ret - tet, ret - tet, schüt - zet
sf
p
f

1st & 2nd LADIES
Back, loath-ly worm, to Hell and die! Re-joice!
Stirb, Un-ge-heu'r, durch uns-re Macht! Tri-umph!
3rd LADY
Back, loath-ly worm, to Hell and die! Re-joice!
Stirb, Un-ge-heu'r, durch uns-re Macht! Tri-umph!
He falls, exhausted.
T.
die!
mich!
f
2 3 1
1. L.
2. L.
Re-joice! 'Tis ours a-lone the
Tri-umph! Sie ist voll-bracht, die
3. L.
Re-joice! 'Tis ours a-lone the
Tri-umph! Sie ist voll-bracht, die
p
1. L.
2. L.
vic-to-ry. To save this youth in dan-ger's
Hel-den-tat. Er ist be-freit, er ist be-
3. L.
vic-to-ry. To save this youth in dan-ger's
Hel-den-tat. Er ist be-freit, er ist be-

1. L.
2. L.
hour 'Twas on - ly vir - tue had the power, 'twas on - ly
freit durch uns - res Ar - mes Tap - fer - keit, durch uns - res
3. L.
hour 'Twas on - ly vir - tue had the power, 'twas on - ly
freit durch uns - res Ar - mes Tap - fer - keit, durch uns - res
vir - tue had the power.
Ar - mes Tap - fer - keit.
vir - tue had the power.
Ar - mes Tap - fer - keit.
p
1st LADY
How come - ly is... this youth and fair!
Ein hol - der Jüngling, sanft und schön!
2nd LADY
How sweet, how
So schön, als
2. L.
gra - cious is his air!
ich noch nie ge - sehn!
3rd LADY
No art could paint a face so
Ja, ja, ge - wiss, zum Ma - len

1st LADY
Ah, were I not to vir - tue bound, My heart its
Würd' ich mein Herz der Lie - be weihn, so müsst' es
2nd LADY
Ah, were I not to vir - tue bound, My heart its
Würd' ich mein Herz der Lie - be weihn, so müsst' es
3. L.
rare! Ah, were I not to vir-tue bound, My heart...... its
schön! Würd' ich mein Herz der Lie-be weihn, so müsst'...... es
1. L.
choice in him had found, my heart its choice in him had found.
die - ser Jüng-ling sein, so müsst' es die - ser Jüng-ling sein.
2. L.
choice in him had found, my heart its choice in him had found.
die - ser Jüng-ling sein, so müsst' es die - ser Jüng-ling sein.
3. L.
choice in him had found, my heart..... its choice in him had found.
die - ser Jüng-ling sein, so müsst' es die - ser Jüng-ling sein.
p
1. L.
Then to the Queen our foot-steps wing-ing, Let us this
Lasst uns zu uns-rer Für-stin ei - len, ihr die-se
2. L.
Then to the Queen our foot-steps wing-ing, Let us this
Lasst uns zu uns-rer Für-stin ei - len, ihr die - se
3. L.
Then to the Queen our foot-steps wing-ing, Let us this
Lasst uns zu uns-rer Für-stin ei - len, ihr die - se
f
p

1. L.
joy - ful news be bring-ing; Per - chance to her un - end - ing
Nach-richt zu er - tei - len; viel - leicht dass die - ser schö - ne
2. L.
joy - ful news be bring-ing; Per - chance to her un - end - ing
Nach-richt zu er - tei - len; viel - leicht dass die - ser schö - ne
3. L.
joy - ful news be bring-ing; Per-chance to her un-end-ing
Nach-richt zu er - tei - len; viel-leicht dass die - ser schö - ne
f
p
1. L.
grief This no - ble youth may bear re-lief, this
Mann die vor' - ge Ruh' ihr ge - ben kann, die
2. L.
grief This no - ble youth may bear re - lief, this
Mann die vor' - ge Ruh' ihr ge - ben kann, die
3. L.
grief This no - ble youth may bear re - lief, this
Mann die vor' - ge Ruh' ihr ge - ben kann, die
1. L.
no - ble youth.......... may bear re - lief.
vor' - ge Ruh'.......... ihr ge - ben kann.
2. L.
no - ble youth may bear re - lief.
vor' - ge Ruh' ihr ge - ben kann.
3. L.
no - ble youth may bear re - lief.
vor' - ge Ruh' ihr ge - ben kann.
p
f

* 1st lady moves DSL next to 3rd lady & returns to previous position

1. L.
2. L.
3. L.
I'll guard him,
Ich wa - che!
I'll guard him,
Ich schüt - ze!
I! I! I!
Ich! ich! ich!
I! I!
Ich! ich!
I!
Ich!
p
f
Allegretto
What! must I go?
Ich soll - te fort?
Not
Ei,

1. L.
2. L.
3. L.
Not I,............ no, no, not I, not
Ei, ei,........... ei, ei! wie fein, wie
Not I, no, no, not I, not
Ei, ei, ei, ei! wie fein, wie
I, no, no, not I, not
ei, ei, ei! wie fein, wie
I, no, no, not I! Since each a-lone with him would stay, with him would stay, Of
fein! ei, ei! wie fein! Sie wä-ren gern bei ihm al-lein, bei ihm al-lein. Nein,
I, no, no, not I! Since each a-lone with him would stay, with him would stay,
fein! ei, ei! wie fein! Sie wä-ren gern bei ihm al-lein, bei ihm al-lein.
I, no, no, not I! Since each a-lone with him would stay, with him would stay,
fein! ei, ei! wie fein! Sie wä-ren gern bei ihm al-lein, bei ihm al-lein.
course, of course she finds us in..... the way. Since
nein! nein, nein, nein, nein! das kann nicht sein. Sie
Of course, of course she finds us in..... the way. Since
Nein, nein! nein, nein, nein, nein! das kann nicht sein. Sie
Of course, of course she finds us in the way. Since
Nein, nein! nein, nein, nein, nein! das kann nicht sein. Sie

1. L.
each a-lone with him would stay, with him would stay, Of course, of
wä - ren gern bei ihm al - lein, bei ihm al - lein. Nein, nein! nein,
2. L.
each a-lone with him would stay, with him would stay, Of course,
wä - ren gern bei ihm al - lein, bei ihm al - lein. Nein, nein!
3. L.
each a-lone with him would stay, with him would stay, Of course,
wä - ren gern bei ihm al - lein, bei ihm al - lein. Nein, nein!
1. L.
course she finds us in.... the way,............ she finds us in.... the
nein! nein, nein, das kann nicht sein,............ nein, nein, das kann nicht
2. L.
of course she finds us in.... the way,............ she finds us in.... the
nein, nein! nein, nein, das kann nicht sein,............ nein, nein, das kann nicht
3. L.
of course she finds us in the way,............ she finds us in the
nein, nein! nein, nein, das kann nicht sein,............ nein, nein, das kann nicht
1. L.
way,.............. she finds us in..... the way.
sein,.............. nein, nein, das kann nicht sein!
2. L.
way,............. she finds us in...... the way.
sein,............. nein, nein, das kann nicht sein!
3. L.
way,............. she finds us in the way.
sein,............. nein, nein, das kann nicht sein!

Allegro
2nd LADY
I can con-tain my-self no
Was woll-te ich da-rum nicht
3rd LADY
I can con-tain my-self no lon - ger;
Was woll-te ich da-rum nicht ge - ben,
f p tr
1. L.
I can con-tain my-self no lon - ger;
Was woll-te ich da-rum nicht ge - ben,
2. L.
lon - ger;
ge - ben,
3. L.
My pas-sion fier-cer grows and
könnt' ich mit die-sem Jüng-ling
My pas-sion fier-cer grows and stron - ger;
könnt' ich mit die-sem Jüng-ling le - ben!
stron - ger;
le - ben!

1. L.
2. L.
3. L.
stron - ger;
le - ben!
Could I but be with him a -
Hätt' ich ihn doch so ganz al -
Could I but be with him a - lone,
Hätt' ich ihn doch so ganz al - lein,
but
ihn
Could I but be with him a - lone,
Hätt' ich ihn doch so ganz al - lein,
but
ihn
-lone, with him a-lone, with him a - lone! Yet nei - ther moves; they stand like
-lein, so ganz al-lein, so ganz al - lein! Doch kei - ne geht; es kann nicht
be with him a - lone! Yet nei-ther moves; they
doch so ganz al - lein! Doch kei-ne geht; es
be with him a - lone! Yet nei - ther moves;
doch so ganz al - lein! Doch kei - ne geht;
stone. My on - ly course is to be gone,
sein. Am be-sten ist es, wenn ich geh!
stand like stone. My on - ly course is to be
kann nicht sein. Am be-sten ist es, wenn ich
they stand like stone.
es kann nicht sein.

1. L.
2. L.
3. L.
is
ich
gone,
geh',
My on - ly course is to be gone, my on - ly course is to be gone,
Am be-sten ist es, wenn ich geh', am be-sten ist es, wenn ich geh',
cresc.
to be gone. Fare-well, fare-well, my heart's own joy! Fare-
geh', ich geh'. Du Jüng - ling, schön und lie - be-voll, du
f
p
dolce
-well, farewell, en - tranc - ing boy! My heart will aye be sore To... see...
trau - ter Jüng - ling, le - be wohl! bis ich dich wie-der - seh', bis ich...
To...
bis
f
p

1. L.
2. L.
3. L.
thy face.................. once more,................ to
dich wie - - der - seh', bis
see........................... thy face.... once more,... to
ich........................... dich wie - - der - seh',.... bis
To... see thy face.... once more, to
bis ich dich wie - - der - seh',... bis
see thy.......... face once more....... Fare-well, farewell, my heart's own joy, Fare-
ich dich........ wie - der - seh'......... Du Jüng - ling, schön und lie - be-voll, du
see thy face once more....... Fare-well, farewell, my heart's own joy, Fare-
ich dich wie - der - seh'......... Du Jüng - ling, schön und lie - be-voll, du
p
dolce
-well, farewell, en - tranc - ing boy! My heart will aye be sore To...
trau - ter Jüng - ling, le - be wohl! bis ich dich wie - der - seh', bis
-well, farewell, en - tranc - ing boy! My heart will aye be sore
trau - ter Jüng - ling, le - be wohl! bis ich dich wie - der - seh',
f
p
Move forward again & closer

1. L.
see.. thy face.................... once more,..............
ich.. dich wie - - der - seh',..............
2. L.
To... see......................... thy face..... once
bis... ich......................... dich wie - - der -
3. L.
To see thy face..... once
bis ich dich wie - - der -
1. L.
.... to see thy............ face once more, to
bis ich dich.......... wie - der - seh', bis
2. L.
more,.... to see thy........... face once more, to
- seh',....... bis ich dich......... wie - der - seh', bis
3. L.
more,.... to see thy face once more, to.... see thy...
- seh',....... bis ich dich wie - der - seh', bis ich dich
1. L.
see thy face once more, thy face once more, to
ich dich wie - der - seh', dich wie - der - seh', bis
2. L.
see thy face once more, thy face once more, to
ich dich wie - der - seh', dich wie - der - seh', bis
3. L.
face.... once... more,................. to.... see thy face once more,................. to
wie - der - seh',.................. bis... ich dich wie - der - seh',.................. bis

Tamino: Where am I? The serpent, dead at my feet! *(A pan-pipe is heard off the stage)* Ha! Is that a man coming? *(Retires)*

Tamino: Wo bin ich? Die bösartige Schlange liegt tot zu meinen Füssen! Welche seltsame Gestalt kommt dort auf mich zu?

Nº 2 Song

Andante
p
from behind
PAPAGENO enters singing.
f
PAPAGENO
1. Now tell me, did you e - ver see So queer a kind of man as me? Yet
2. But there's a sport that's fi - ner yet Than traps for sil - ly birds to set; Yes,
1. Der Vo - gel - fän - ger bin ich ja, stets lu - stig, hei - sa hop - sa - sa! Ich
2. Wenn al - le Mäd - chen wä - ren mein, so tausch - te ich brav Zuk - ker ein: die
p

Pap.
young and old... in... ev-'ry place Are al-ways glad to see my face.
bra-ver game there is, I know, And af-ter it I mean to go.
Vo-gel-fän-ger bin be-kannt bei Alt und Jung im gan-zen Land.
wel-che mir am lieb-sten wär, der gäb' ich gleich den Zuk-ker her.
Pap.
I spread my nets and whis-tle clear To catch the birds as
I'd glad-ly ply the fow-ler's trade If I could catch a...
Weiss mit dem Lok-ken um-zu-geh'n und mich aufs Pfei-fen
Und küss-te sie mich zärt-lich dann, wär' sie mein Weib und
(plays his pipe)
Pap.
they come near,
pret-ty maid.
zu ver-stehn!
ich ihr Mann.
And from this cage they can-not stir, For
Then who would share the cage with her? Why,
Drum kann ich froh und lu-stig sein, denn
Sie schlief an mei-ner Sei-te ein, ich
(plays)
D.S.
Pap.
I'm the jol-ly bird catch-er.
sure, the jol-ly bird catch-er!
al-le Vö-gel sind ja mein.
wieg-te wie ein Kind sie ein.
D.S.
Fine

Tamino: You merry fellow, tell me, who are you?

Papageno: Who am I? why, a man like yourself, of course. And who are you?

Tamino: I am the Prince Tamino.

Papageno: Prince? What's that?

Tamino: My father is a King and rules over wide lands and much people; that is why I am called a Prince.

Papageno: Lands? people? a prince? Tell me then, are there other lands and other people beyond those hills?

Tamino: Yes, thousands and thousands.

Papageno: Then perhaps I might go and sell my birds there.

Tamino: But tell me, what is this country? Who is king over it?

Papageno: I don't know.

Tamino: Where do you come from?

Papageno: I don't know.

Tamino: How do you live, then?

Papageno: By eating and drinking, of course, like any one else. I catch birds for the Queen of Night and her ladies, who give me food and drink in exchange.

Tamino: The Queen of Night?

Papageno: (*Aside.*) How he stares at me! I'm quite frightened. (*To Tamino*): Why do you look at me like that?

Tamino: Well, I'm not so sure that you are a man after all.

Papageno: Not a man? Why not?

Tamino: With all those feathers, you look more like——

Papageno: Like one of my own birds? Have a care what you say. I have a giant's strength! (*Aside*): If that does not frighten him away, I shall have to run away myself.

Tamino: Then perhaps it was you that killed the serpent, and saved my life?

Papageno: What serpent? (*Sees the serpent and starts.*) Oh! is it alive?

Tamino: How did you kill it? You have no weapons.

Papageno: What should I want with weapons? (*Shows his arms.*)

Tamino: You throttled it?

Papageno: Of course I throttled it. (*Aside.*) I never knew I was so strong.

Tamino: Sag' mir, du lustiger Freund, wer du bist!

Papageno: Wer ich bin? Ein Mensch wie du. Wenn ich dich nun fragte, wer du bist?

Tamino: So würde ich dir antworten, dass ich aus fürstlichem Geblüte bin.

Papageno: Das ist mir zu hoch. Musst dich deutlicher erklären, wenn ich dich verstehen soll!

Tamino: Mein Vater ist Fürst, der über viele Länder und Menschen herrscht; darum nennt man mich Prinz.

Papageno: Länder? Menschen? Prinz? Sag' du mir zuvor: giebt's ausser diesen Bergen auch noch Länder und Menschen?

Tamino: Viele Tausende!

Papageno: Da liess' sich eine Spekulation mit meinen Vögeln machen.

Tamino: Wie nennt man eigentlich diese Gegend? Wer beherrscht sie?

Papageno: Das kann ich dir ebensowenig beantworten, als ich weiss, wie ich auf die Welt gekommen bin.

Tamino: Wie? Du wüsstest nicht, wo du geboren, oder wer deine Eltern waren?

Papageno: Kein Wort!

Tamino: Aber wie lebst du?

Papageno: Von Essen und Trinken wie alle Menschen. Ich fange für die sternflammende Königin und ihre Jungfrauen verschiedene Vögel; dafür erhalt' ich täglich Speis' und Trank von ihr.

Tamino: Sternflammende Königin?

Papageno: Wie er mich so starr anblickt! Bald fang' ich an, mich vor ihm zu fürchten. Warum siehst du so verdächtig und schelmisch nach mir?

Tamino: Weil—weil ich zweifle, ob du ein Mensch bist.

Papageno: Wie war das?

Tamino: Nach deinen Federn, die dich bedecken, halt' ich dich——

Papageno: Doch für keinen Vogel? Bleib' zurück, sag' ich, und traue mir nicht; denn ich habe Riesenkraft. Wenn er sich nicht bald von mir schrecken lässt, so lauf' ich davon.

Tamino: Riesenkraft? Also warst du wohl gar mein Erretter, der diese giftige Schlange bekämpfte?

Papageno: Schlange? Ist sie tot oder lebendig?

Tamino: Freund, wie hast du dieses Ungeheuer bekämpft? Du bist ohne Waffen!

Papageno: Brauch' keine!

Tamino: Du hast sie also erdrosselt?

Papageno: Erdrosselt! Bin in meinem Leben nicht so stark gewesen als heute.

(*Enter the Three Ladies, veiled.*)

3 *Ladies:* (*All together.*) Papageno!

Papageno: Ha! That's meant for me. (*To Tamino.*) Look there, friend!

Tamino: Who are those ladies?

Papageno: I don't know. They take my birds every day, and give me wine, bread, and fruit in exchange for them.

Tamino: They must surely be very beautiful.

Papageno: No, no, if they were beautiful, they wouldn't hide their faces.

3 *Ladies:* Papageno!

Papageno: Beautiful? I never saw anything lovelier in all my life. (*Aside.*) That will please them.

3 *Ladies:* Papageno!

Papageno: (*Aside.*) What have I done to make them so angry? (*To the ladies*): Fair ladies, here are your birds.

1*st Lady:* No wine for you to-day, Papageno—only cold water.

2*nd Lady:* No bread for you to-day, Papageno—only a stone.

3*rd Lady:* No fruit for you to-day, Papageno—you are to have your mouth locked up with this padlock. (*She locks up his mouth.*)

1*st Lady:* Do you wish to know why the Queen has ordered you to be punished in this way? (*Papageno nods.*)

2*nd Lady:* So that you may tell no more lies to strangers.

3*rd Lady:* Tell us, did you kill the serpent? (*Papageno shakes his head.*)

2*nd Lady:* Who did, then? (*Papageno signifies that he does not know.*)

1*st Lady:* Prince, it was we who saved you. Our mistress, the Queen of Night, sends you this portrait of her daughter. Should the sight of those features leave you not utterly indifferent, there awaits you a great and glorious future. We meet again!

(*Exeunt Three Ladies, followed by Papageno.*)

3 *Damen:* Papageno!

Papageno: Aha, das geht mich an! Sieh dich um, Freund!

Tamino: Wer sind diese Damen?

Papageno: Wer sie eigentlich sind, weiss ich selbst nicht. Ich weiss nur so viel, dass sie mir täglich meine Vögel abnehmen und mir dafür Wein, Zuckerbrot und süsse Feigen bringen.

Tamino: Sie sind vermutlich sehr schön?

Papageno: Ich denke nicht! Denn wenn sie schön wären, würden sie ihre Gesichter nicht bedecken.

3 *Damen:* Papageno!

Papageno: Sei still! Sie drohen mir schon. Du fragst, ob sie schön sind, und ich kann dir darauf nichts antworten, als dass ich in meinem Leben nichts Reizenderes sah. Jetzt werden sie bald wieder gut werden.

3 *Damen:* Papageno!

Papageno: Was muss ich denn heute verbrochen haben, dass sie so aufgebracht wider mich sind? Hier, meine Schönen, übergeb' ich meine Vögel.

1. *Dame:* Dafür schickt dir unsere Fürstin heute zum ersten Mal statt Wein reines helles Wasser.

2. *Dame:* Und mir befahl sie, dass ich statt Zuckerbrot diesen Stein dir überbringen soll.

3. *Dame:* Und statt der süssen Feigen hab' ich die Ehre, dir dies goldene Schloss vor den Mund zu schlagen.

1. *Dame:* Du willst vermutlich wissen, warum die Fürstin dich heute so wunderbar bestraft? (*Papageno bejaht es durch Nicken mit dem Kopf.*)

2. *Dame:* Damit du künftig nie mehr Fremde belügst.

3. *Dame:* Und dass du dich nie der Heldentaten rühmst, die andere vollzogen.

1. *Dame:* Sag' an, hast du diese Schlange bekämpft ? (*Papageno verneint durch Schütteln mit dem Kopfe.*)

2. *Dame:* Wer denn also? (*Papageno deutet, dass er es nicht weiss.*)

3. *Dame:* Wir waren's, Jüngling, die dich befreiten. Hier, dies Gemälde schickt dir die grosse Fürstin; es ist das Bildnis ihrer Tochter. Findest du, dass diese Züge dir nicht gleichgültig sind, dann ist Glück, Ehr' und Ruhm dein Los! Auf Wiedersehen!

Nº 3 Aria

Larghetto
TAMINO
O love - li-ness beyond compare! Was e - ver maiden half so
Dies Bildniss ist be-zaubernd schön, wie noch kein Au-ge je ge -
p
T.
fair? I know not, I know not if 'tis joy or pain That o - verwhelms my reeling
sehn! Ich fühl' es, ich fühl' es, wie dies Göt-ter-bild mein Herz...... mit neu - er Re-gung
sfp
T.
brain, that o - ver-whelms my reel-ing brain. I...
füllt, mein Herz...... mit neu - er Re - gung füllt. Dies
dolce
T.
know not what is this e - mo-tion, That fires my heart with strange de - vo-tion;
Et - was kann ich zwar nicht nennen, doch fühl' ich's hier wie Feu - er brennen.

T.
Can it be love that leads me on?
Soll die Em-pfin-dung Lie-be sein?
can it be love.... that leads me on?
soll die Em-pfin-dung Lie-be sein?
mf
p
Ah yes, it must be love a - lone, it must be, it must be, it
Ja, ja, die Lie - be ist's al - lein, die Lie-be, die Lie-be, die
cresc.
mf
p
sfp
must...... be love a - lone.
Lie - be ist's al - lein.
f
p
cresc.
f p
Oh could I on - ly kneel be - fore......... her, Tell her how mad - ly I a -
O, wenn ich sie nur fin - den könn - te! O, wenn sie doch schon vor mir
cresc.
f p
cresc.
- dore.......... her! And fear - ing, hop - ing—
stün - de! Ich wür - de, wür - de,
f p

T.
maid di - vine! Ah, what would I?— With - in these
warm und rein, was wür - de ich? Ich wür - de
Ped.
arms I would en - fold her, To this my burn - ing... heart fast
sie... voll... Ent - zük - ken an die - sen heis - sen... Bu - sen
cresc.
hold her, And so for e - ver were she mine, and so .... for e - ver were she
drük - ken, und e - wig wä - re sie dann mein, und e - wig wä - re sie dann
mine, and so .... for e - ver were she mine,... so for e - ver were she
mein, und e - wig wä - re sie dann mein,... e - wig wä - re sie dann
mine,... so for e - ver were she mine.
mein,... e - wig wä - re.. sie dann mein.

(Re-enter the Three Ladies.)

1st Lady: Prince, the Queen has heard your every word——

2nd Lady: She has read your every look——

3rd Lady: She has resolved to make you the happiest man on earth. If you are as chivalrous as you are passionate, it will be your privilege to effect the rescue of her most unhappy daughter, Pamina.

Tamino: Pamina! Pamina unhappy?

1st Lady: Yes, alas! an evil magician has carried her off, and holds her in durance vile.

Tamino: His name!

2nd Lady: Sarastro!

3rd Lady: The high priest of the Sun.

Tamino: Pamina a prisoner in his hands? Ladies by the fire that burns within me, I swear to be her deliverer. Lead on!

1st Lady: Brave youth! *(Thunder.)*

2nd Lady: She comes! *(Thunder.)*

3rd Lady: The Queen! *(Thunder.)*

1. *Dame:* Rüste dich mit Mut und Standhaftigkeit, schöner Jüngling! Die Fürstin hat jedes deiner Worte gehört; sie hat——

2. *Dame:* jeden Zug in deinem Gesichte gelesen; ihr mütterliches Herz——

3. *Dame:* hat beschlossen, dich ganz glücklich zu machen. Hat dieser Jüngling, sprach sie, auch so viel Mut und Tapferkeit, als er zärtlich ist, o, so ist meine Tochter ganz gewiss gerettet.

Tamino: Gerettet? Was hör ich?

1. *Dame:* Wisse, ein böser Dämon hat Pamina ihr entrissen!

Tamino: O Pamina, du mir entrissen! Kommt Mädchen, führt mich! Sie sei gerettet! Das schwöre ich bei meiner Liebe, bei meinem Herzen! *(Donner.)* Ihr Götter, was ist das?

3 *Damen:* Fasse dich!

1. *Dame:* Es verkündet die Ankunft unserer Königin. *(Donner.)*

3 *Damen:* Sie kommt! *(Donner.)* Sie kommt! *(Donner.)* Sie kommt!

Nº 4 Recitative and Aria

Qu.
To thee a-lone can turn in de-so - la-tion The Queen of highest
Ein Jüngling, so wie du, vermag am be-sten das tief-gebeugte
cresc.
ARIA
Larghetto
Qu.
Heav'n for con-so-la-tion. All joy.... from me has now de-part-ed; How can I
Mut- terherz zu trösten. Zum Lei - den bin ich aus-er - ko-ren, denn mei-ne
Qu.
e'er for-get that day.... Which from her mother bro-ken - heart - ed My daughter all un-will-ing
Toch - ter feh-let mir. Durch sie ging all mein Glück ver-lo - ren, durch sie ging all mein Glück ver-
Qu.
part-ed? My bitt'rest foe, my bit - - t'rest foe snatch'd her a-
- lo - ren, ein Bö - se-wicht, ein Bö - - se-wicht ent-floh mit
Qu.
- way. What hor-ror came o'er me! my prayers un - a -
ihr. Noch seh' ich ihr Zit-tern mit ban - gem Er -

Qu.
-vail-ing, I heard her pro-test-ing, be-seech-ing, be-
-schüt-tern, ihr ängst-li-ches Be-ben, ihr schüch-ter-nes
Qu.
-wail-ing; Be-fore my eyes I saw him seize.. her; O..... help! O..... help!
Stre-ben. Ich muss-te sie mir rau-ben se-hen! Ach... helft! ach helft!
p
tr
fp
fp
Qu.
can I for-get that cry? Not all my tears could e'er re-lease her, A-gainst his craft... no
war alles was sie sprach; al-lein ver-ge-bens war mein Flehen, denn mei-ne Hül-fe
p
Qu.
power had I, a-gainst his craft, a-gainst his craft no power... had
war zu schwach, denn mei-ne Hül-fe, mei-ne Hül-fe war...... zu
Allegro moderato
Qu.
I. Thou, Prince, thou with
schwach. Du, du, du sollst
f
p

Qu.
man-ly.... ar-dour burn-est, Thou shalt to me my child re-
sie zu be-frei-en ge - hen, du wirst der Toch-ter Ret - ter
Qu.
-store, yes, thou..... shalt to me.... my... child re - store;
sein, ja, du........wirst der Toch-ter... Ret - ter sein.
f
p
cresc.
f
Qu.
And when vic - to - rious thou re - turn - est, I plight her
Und werd' ich dich als... Sie - ger... se - hen, so sei sie
p
Qu.
thine for... e - ver - more, I plight her thine
dann auf.. e - wig... dein, so sei sie dann
Qu.
fp

Tamino: Am I dreaming? *(Looks at the portrait.)*
No — it cannot be.

Tamino: Ist's denn auch Wirklichkeit, was ich sah?
O ihr guten Götter, täuscht mich nicht.

Nº 5 Quintet

Allegro
PAPAGENO enters, pointing to his mouth and trying to speak.
Hm, hm, hm, hm, hm, hm, hm, hm, hm, hm, hm, hm, hm, hm, hm,
Hm, hm, hm, hm, hm, hm, hm, hm, hm, hm, hm, hm, hm, hm, hm,
f
p
tr
TAMINO
'Tis hard such pun-ish-ment to suf-fer; thy lips are tight lock'd up, I see;
Der Ar-me kann von Stra-fe sa-gen, denn sei-ne Spra-che ist da-hin.
Pap.
hm!
hm!
Hm, hm, hm,
Hm, hm, hm,
T.
To loose thy bonds I'd glad-ly
Ich kann nichts tun, als dich be-
Pap.
hm, hm, hm, hm, hm, hm, hm, hm, hm, hm, hm, hm, hm!
hm, hm, hm, hm, hm, hm, hm, hm, hm, hm, hm, hm, hm!
T.
of-fer, but have no pow'r to...set thee free, To loose thy bonds
-kla-gen, weil ich zu schwach zu..hel-fen bin. Ich kann nichts tun,..
Pap.
Hm, hm, hm, hm, hm, hm, hm,
Hm, hm, hm, hm, hm, hm, hm,

T.
Pap.
I'd glad-ly of-fer, But have no pow'r to set thee free,
als dich be - kla-gen, weil ich zu schwach zu hel - fen bin,
hm, hm, hm, hm, hm, Hm, hm, hm,
hm, hm, hm, hm, hm, Hm, hm, hm,
I have no pow'r..... to set thee free, I have no pow'r to set thee free.
weil ich zu schwach zu hel-fen bin, weil ich zu schwach zu hel-fen bin.
hm,hm,hm,hm, hm,hm,hm,hm, hm,hm, hm,hm, hm, hm, hm, hm, hm, hm, hm,hm, hm.
hm,hm,hm,hm, hm,hm,hm,hm, hm,hm, hm,hm, hm, hm, hm, hm, hm, hm, hm,hm, hm.
Enter the THREE LADIES
1st LADY
Our gra-cious Queen her par - don sends, If thou wilt strive to make a - mends.
Die Kö - ni - gin be-gna-digt dich, er-lässt die Stra-fe dir.. durch mich.
She removes the padlock from PAPAGENO's mouth.
2nd LADY
Re - mem-ber, 'tis no
Ja, plaud-re, lüge
PAPAGENO
Oh joy, once more I'm free to chat - ter!
Nun plaudert Pa - pa - ge - no wie - der!

1. L.
2. L.
laughing mat-ter!
nur nicht wie-der!
Thou'lt ne'er for-get that pad-lock's pain,
Dies Schloss soll dei-ne War-nung sein,
3rd LADY
Thou'lt ne'er for-get that pad-lock's pain,
Dies Schloss soll dei-ne War-nung sein,
Pap.
No lie shall pass my lips a-gain; I'll
Ich lü-ge nimmer-mehr, nein, nein! Dies
tr
No, no, thou'lt ne'er for-get that pad-lock's pain.
soll dei-ne Warnung, dei-ne War-nung sein.
3. L.
No, no, thou'lt ne'er for-get that pad-lock's pain.
soll dei-ne Warnung, dei-ne War-nung sein.
ne'er for-get that pad-lock's pain, for-get that pad-lock's pain.
Schloss soll mei-ne War-nung sein, soll mei-ne War-nung sein.
cresc.
f
p
sotto voce
If ly-ing lips could all be fet-ter'd And made se-cure with
Be-kä-men doch die Lügner al-le ein sol-ches Schloss vor
TAMINO sotto voce

1. L.
2. L.
lock and key, Then false-hood's hate-ful might were shatter'd, And man with
ih - ren Mund! Statt Hass, Ver - leumdung, schwarzer Galle be-stän-de
3. L.
lock and key, Then false-hood's hate-ful might were shatter'd, And man with
ih - ren Mund! Statt Hass, Ver - leumdung, schwarzer Galle be-stän-de
T.
lock and key, Then false-hood's hate-ful might were shatter'd, And man with
ih - ren Mund! Statt Hass, Ver - leumdung, schwarzer Galle be-stän-de
Pap.
lock and key, Then false-hood's hate-ful might were shatter'd,
ih - ren Mund! Statt Hass, Ver - leumdung, schwarzer Galle

1. L.
2. L.
man at peace could be, Then false-hood's hate-ful might were shatter'd,
Lieb' und Bru - der-bund, statt Hass, Ver - leumdung, schwarzer Galle
3. L.
man at peace could be, Then false-hood's hate-ful might were shatter'd,
Lieb' und Bru - der-bund, statt Hass, Ver - leumdung, schwarzer Galle
T.
man at peace could be, Then false-hood's hate-ful might were shatter'd,
Lieb' und Bru - der-bund, statt Hass, Ver - leumdung, schwarzer Galle
Pap.
at peace could be, Then false-hood's hate-ful might were shatter'd,
und Bru - der-bund, statt Hass, Ver - leumdung, schwarzer Galle

1st LADY
1.L.
2.L.
3.L.
T.
Pap.
And man with man at... peace could be.
be-stän-de Lieb' und Bru-der-bund.
O
O
And man with man at peace could be.
be-stän-de Lieb' und Bru-der-bund.
hands TAMINO a golden flute.
Prince, our Queen this gift be-stows, Since thy de-vo-tion well she knows:
Prinz, nimm dies Geschenk von mir. Dies sen-det uns-re Für-stin dir!
She deigns the ma-gic flute to send thee; In ev-'ry
Die Zau-ber-flö-te wird dich schützen, im gröss-ten
pe-ril 'twill de-fend thee. Un-bound-ed pow'r to him is grant-ed Who sounds a-
Un-glück un-ter-stüt-zen. Hie-mit kannst du allmächtig handeln, der Men-schen
Un-bound-ed pow'r to him is grant-ed Who sounds a-
Hie-mit kannst du allmächtig handeln, der Men-schen
p
fp

1.L.
2.L.
-right its notes en-chant-ed; The deep-est grief to... joy 'twill
Lei-denschaft ver-wandeln; der Trau-ri-ge wirdfreu-dig
3.L.
-right its notes en-chant-ed; The deep-est grief to joy 'twill
Lei-denschaft ver-wandeln; der Trau-ri-ge wird freu-dig
mf
p
1.L.
2.L.
turn, Make hardest heart with love... to burn.
sein, den Ha-ge-stolz nimmt Lie-be ein.
3.L.
turn, Make hardest heart with love to burn.
sein, den Ha-ge-stolz nimmt Lie-be ein.
f
p
Ped.
sotto voce
1.L.
2.L.
Yes, 'tis on-ly mu-sic That has the power to weave that
O so ei-ne Flö-te ist mehr als Gold und Kro-nen
sotto voce
3.L.
Yes, 'tis on-ly mu-sic That has the power to weave that
O so ei-ne Flö-te ist mehr als Gold und Kro-nen
TAMINO sotto voce
Yes, 'tis on-ly mu-sic That has the power to weave that
O so ei-ne Flö-te ist mehr als Gold und Kro-nen
PAPAGENO sotto voce
Yes, 'tis on-ly mu-sic That has the power to weave that
O so ei-ne Flö-te ist mehr als Gold und Kro-nen

That all in
und... Zu -
1.L.
2.L.
spell, Jar - ring souls so to at - tune all in
wert, denn.. durch sie wird Menschen - glück und Zu -
3.L.
spell, Jar - ring souls so to at - tune all in
wert, denn durch sie wird Menschen-glück und Zu -
T.
spell, Jar - ring souls.................. so to at - tune........................ all in
wert, denn durch sie..................... wird Menschen - glück....................... und Zu -
Pap.
spell, Jar - ring souls so to at - tune all in
wert, denn durch sie wird Menschen-glück und Zu -
1.L.
2.L.
f
p
p
har - mo - ny may dwell,....................... in har - mo - ny may
-frie - den - heit ver - mehrt,....................... wird Men - schenglück ver -
3.L.
f
p
har - mo - ny may dwell, in har - mo - ny may
-frie - den - heit ver - mehrt, wird Men - schenglück ver -
T.
f
p
har - mo - ny may dwell, in har - mo - ny may
-frie - den - heit ver - mehrt, wird Men - schen-glück ver -
Pap.
f
p
har - mo - ny may dwell, in har - mo - ny may
-frie - den - heit ver - mehrt, wird Men - schen - glück ver -
f
p

1.L.
2.L.
3.L.
T.
Pap.
dwell,.................. in har - mo - ny may dwell.
mehrt,.................. Zu - frie - den-heit ver - mehrt.
dwell, in har - mo - ny may dwell.
mehrt, Zu - frie - den-heit ver - mehrt.
dwell, in har - mo - ny may dwell.
mehrt, Zu - frie - den-heit ver - mehrt.
dwell, in har - mo - ny may dwell.
mehrt, Zu - frie - den - heit ver-mehrt.
PAPAGENO
La-dies fair, with your per-mis-sion, May I take my
Nun, ihr schö-nen Frau-en - zim-mer, darf ich, so em-
1st & 2nd LADIES
Nay, but hear this new com - mis-sion That the Queen would have thee
Dich em - pfeh - len kannst du im - mer, doch be-stimmt die Für-stin
3rd LADY
Nay, but hear this new com - mis-sion That the Queen would have thee
Dich em - pfeh - len kannst du im - mer, doch be-stimmt die Für-stin
Pap.
leave of you?
-pfehl'ich mich.

1.L.
2.L.
do; With the Prince she'd have thee fa-ring, All his dan-gers with him
dich, mit dem Prin-zen ohn' Ver-wei-len nach Sa-ra-stros Burg zu
3.L.
do; With the Prince she'd have thee fa-ring, All his dan-gers with him
dich, mit dem Prin-zen ohn' Ver-wei-len nach Sa-ra-stros Burg zu
1.L.
2.L.
sha-ring.
ei-len.
3.L.
sha-ring.
ei-len.
PAPAGENO
Face Sa-ras-tro? No, not I! You yourselves to me have sworn, If to
Nein, da-für be-dank ich mich! Von euch selb-sten hör-te ich, dass er
f
p
Pap.
en-ter I should try, Where his sa-vage guards are post-ed, He would have me pluck'd and
wie ein Ti-ger-tier. Si-cher liess ohn' al-le Gnaden mich Sa-ra-stro rup-fen,
Pap.
roast-ed, pluck'd and roast-ed, pluck'd and roast-ed, Or by dogs to pie-ces
bra-ten, rup-fen, bra-ten, rup-fen, bra-ten, setz-te mich den Hun-den
cresc.
f
p
cresc.

1st & 2nd LADIES
Nay, on the Prince a - lone re - ly, No harm can come while he is
Dich schützt der Prinz, trau' ihm al - lein! Da-für sollst du sein Die - ner
3rd LADY
Nay, on the Prince a - lone re - ly, No harm can come while he is
Dich schützt der Prinz, trau' ihm al - lein! Da-für sollst du sein Die - ner
Pap.
torn.
für.
f f p
1.L.
2.L.
nigh.
sein.
3.L.
nigh.
sein.
Pap.
Re - ly on him? the De - vil take him! My life too dear I
Dass doch der Prinz beim Teu - fel wä - re! Mein Le - ben ist mir
mfp
Pap.
hold: He'll run a - way, or I mis - take him, 'Twill be just as I fore -
lieb. Am En - de schleicht, bei mei - ner Eh - re, er von mir wie ein
1st LADY
She hands PAPAGENO
See what the Queen has sent for thee.
Hier, nimm dies Klein - od, es sei dein.
Pap.
-told.
Dieb.
A-
Ei,

a chime of bells.
1. L.
2. L.
A peal of bells with ma-gic jin-gle.
Dar-in-nen hörst du Glöckchen tö-nen.
3. L.
A peal of bells with ma-gic jin-gle.
Dar-in-nen hörst du Glöckchen tö-nen.
Pap.
-ha! what-e-ver can it be? To make them
ei! was mag dar-in-nen sein? Werd' ich sie
1. L.
2. L.
sotto voce
Then ring a-main and mer-ry be. Flute for
O ganz ge-wiss, ja, ja, ge-wiss! Sil-ber-
3. L.
sotto voce
Then ring a-main and mer-ry be. Flute for
O ganz ge-wiss, ja, ja, ge-wiss! Sil-ber-
TAMINO sotto voce
Flute for
Sil-ber-
Pap.
sotto voce
ring my fin-gers tin-gle. Flute for
auch wohl spie-len kön-nen? Sil-ber-
p
1. L.
2. L.
mu-sic, bells for laughter, Best of com-rades now or
-glöckchen, Zau-ber-flö-ten sind zu eu-rem Schutz von-
3. L.
mu-sic, bells for laughter, Best of com-rades now....... or
-glöckchen, Zau-ber-flö-ten sind zu eu-rem Schutz... von-
T.
mu-sic, bells for laughter, Best of com-rades now....... or
-glöckchen, Zau-ber-flö-ten sind zu uns-rem Schutz... von-
Pap.
mu-sic, bells for laughter, Best of com-rades now....... or
-glöckchen, Zau-ber-flö-ten sind zu uns-rem Schutz... von-
mf
p
mf
p

1. L.
2. L.
3. L.
T.
Pap.
f
p
sfp
sf
after! Trust them well, they bear a charm Safe to
-nö-ten. Le - bet wohl! wir wol - len gehn. Le - bet
keep you both from harm, safe to keep you
wohl, auf Wie - der - sehn, le - bet wohl, auf
keep us both from harm, safe to keep us
wohl, auf Wie - der - sehn, le - bet wohl, auf

1. L.
2. L.
both from harm.
Wie - der - sehn!
3. L.
both from harm.
Wie - der - sehn!
T.
both from harm. But, la-dies, I en-treat you, say_
Wie - der - sehn! Doch, schöne Da-men, sa-get an,
Pap.
both from harm. What road to take, how find the
Wie - der - sehn! wie man die Burg wohl fin-den
T.
what road to take, how find the way, what road to
wie man die Burg wohl fin-den kann, wie man die
Pap.
way? what road to take, how find the way, what road to
kann? wie man die Burg wohl fin-den kann, wie man die
Andante
1st & 2nd LADIES sotto voce
Three
Drei
3rd LADY sotto voce
Three
Drei
T.
take, how find the way?
Burg wohl fin-den kann?
Pap.
take, how find the way?
Burg wohl fin-den kann?
Andante
p

1. L.
2. L.
gen-tle spi-rits shall pro-tect you,And in the way of truth di-rect you;Their
Knäbchen, jung,schön,hold und wei-se, um-schwe-ben euch auf eu-rer Rei-se; sie
3. L.
gen-tle spi-rits shall pro-tect you,And in the way of truth di-rect you;Their
Knäbchen, jung,schön,hold und wei-se, um-schwe-ben euch auf eu-rer Rei-se; sie
coun-sel they will lend at... need, On-ly to them shall you give heed.
wer-den eu-re Füh-rer sein, folgt ihrem Ra-te ganz al-lein.
coun-sel they will lend at need, On-ly to them shall you give heed.
wer-den eu-re Füh-rer sein, folgt ihrem Ra-te ganz al-lein.
TAMINO
Three
Drei
PAPAGENO
Three
Drei
sf
p
Their
Sie
Their
Sie
T.
gen-tle spi-rits shall pro-tect us,And in the way of truth di-rect us;
Knäb-chen, jung,schön, hold und wei-se, um-schwe-ben uns auf uns-rer Rei-se;
Pap.
gen-tle spi-rits shall pro-tect us,And in the way of truth di-rect us;
Knäb-chen, jung,schön, hold und wei-se, um-schwe-ben uns auf uns-rer Rei-se;

1. L.
2. L.
coun - sel they will lend at... need, On - ly to them shall you give heed.
wer - den eu - re Füh - rer sein, folgt ihrem Ra - te ganz al - lein.
3. L.
coun - sel they will lend at need, On - ly to them shall you give heed.
wer - den eu - re Füh - rer sein, folgt ihrem Ra - te ganz al - lein.
T.
So
So
Pap.
So
So
sf p
1. L.
2. L.
f
So may you soon your
So le - bet wohl! wir
3. L.
f
So may you soon your
So le - bet wohl! wir
T.
f
may we soon our end at - tain, Farewell! farewell! we meet a - gain, so may we soon our
le - bet wohl! wir wol - len gehn, lebt wohl! lebt wohl! auf Wie-dersehn! so le - bet wohl! wir
Pap.
f
may we soon our end at - tain, Farewell! farewell! we meet a - gain, so may we soon our
le - bet wohl! wir wol - len gehn, lebt wohl! lebt wohl! auf Wie-dersehn! so le - bet wohl! wir
sfp
f
p
f

1. L.
2. L.
end at-tain, Fare-well! fare-well! we meet a - gain, we meet a - gain,
wol - len gehn, lebt wohl! lebt wohl! auf Wie - der - sehn, auf Wie - der - sehn,
3. L.
end at-tain, Fare-well! fare-well! we meet a - gain, we meet a - gain,
wol - len gehn, lebt wohl! lebt wohl! auf Wie - der - sehn, auf Wie - der - sehn,
T.
end at-tain, Fare-well! fare-well! we meet a - gain, we
wol - len gehn, lebt wohl! lebt wohl! auf Wie - der - sehn, auf
Pap.
end at-tain, Fare-well! fare-well! we meet a - gain, we
wol - len gehn, lebt wohl! lebt wohl! auf Wie - der - sehn, auf
1. L.
2. L.
we meet a - gain.
auf Wie - der-sehn.
3. L.
we meet a - gain.
auf Wie-der-sehn.
T.
meet a - gain, we meet a - gain.
Wie - der-sehn, auf Wie-der-sehn.
Pap.
meet a - gain, we meet a - gain.
Wie-der-sehn, auf Wie-der-sehn.

Scene 2. A splendid room in the Egyptian style.

Nº 6. Terzetto

Pam.
heart thy words to hear.
Gram ganz si - - cher - lich.
MONOSTATOS claps his hands. Enter Slaves.
M.
Bring chains and make her
He, Skla - ven, legt ihr
The Slaves chain PAMINA.
Oh slay me, ra - ther
O... lass mich lie - ber
hands secure! I'll force thee to o - bey me,
Fes-seln an! Mein Hass soll dich ver-der-ben!
cresc.
f
p
She sinks unconscious.
slay me! Or must.... I.......... worse.................... than death en-dure?
ster-ben, weil nichts, Bar - bar,...................... dich rüh-ren kann!
She's
Nun
cresc.
f
f
MONOSTATOS signs to the Slaves to depart.
mine at last! Now is my conquest sure.
fort, nun fort! Lasst mich bei ihr al - lein!
p
p

PAPAGENO puts his head in.
PAPAGENO
What place is this?
Wo bin ich wohl?
Pap.
where have I stray'd?
Wo mag ich sein?
Just now I heard a clatter; Well,
A - ha! da find ich Leute. Ge-
Pap.
He enters.
well, I'm not a-fraid.
-wagt, ich geh' hin-ein.
MONOSTATOS and PAPAGENO catch sight of each other simultaneously.
Pap.
Good morrow, pret-ty maid;
Schön Mädchen, jung und fein,
Come, tell me what's the matter?
viel weisser noch als Kreide.
f

(each is terrified at the other)
M.
Ah! That is the De - vil cer - tain - ly! That is the
Hu! das ist der Teu - fel si - cher - lich, das ist der
Pap.
Ah! That is the De - vil cer - tain - ly! That is the
Hu! das ist der Teu - fel si - cher - lich, das ist der
p
M.
De - vil cer - tain - ly! Have mer - cy! he's
Teu - fel si - cher - lich. Hab' Mit - leid! Ver -
Pap.
De - vil cer - tain - ly! Have mer - cy! he's come for me!
Teu - fel si - cher - lich. Hab' Mit - leid! Ver - scho - ne mich!
MONOSTATOS and PAPAGENO run off in opposite directions.
M.
come for me! Hoo! Hoo! Hoo! Hoo!
-scho - ne mich! Hu! Hu! Hu! Hu!
Pap.
Hoo! Hoo! Hoo! Hoo!
Hu! Hu! Hu! Hu!

Pamina (*recovers herself*)*:* Mother! Mother! Oh, shall I never escape that cruel Moor?

Papageno (*re-entering*)*:* What a fool I was to be frightened! I've seen plenty of black birds in my life, so why shouldn't there be black men too? (*Sees Pamina.*) Ah! there's the pretty maid still. (*To Pamina.*) Are you the daughter of the Queen of Night?

Pamina: Yes.

Papageno: Then I have news for you. The Queen has sent me——

Pamina (*eagerly*)*:* My mother sent you? But who are you? What is your name?

Papageno: Papageno.

Pamina: Papageno? Papageno? Yes, I remember I used to hear about you, though I never saw you.

Papageno: I'm her Majesty's bird-catcher! I was bringing my birds to the palace early this morning, when I met a strange young man who calls himself a prince. Your mother took a great fancy to him, gave him your portrait, and told him to go and rescue you. As soon as he set eyes on the portrait, he fell in love with you, and swore he would never rest till he had found you.

Pamina: He fell in love with me?

Papageno: We set out at once, and here we are.

Pamina: But when Sarastro comes back and finds you here——

Papageno: He's out? Then there's not a moment to lose. Come, let's run away at once, and find the young prince.

Pamina: The young prince! He—fell in love with me, you said?

Papageno: Yes—and I believe you've fallen in love with him without seeing even so much as his portrait. And nobody ever falls in love with me.

Pamina: Poor Papageno! You must be very unhappy!

Papageno: I should think I was! If I can't find a wife I shall pluck out all my feathers one by one and then die.

Pamina: No, no, Papageno; take heart—I'm sure everyone finds somebody to love them sooner or later.

Pamina: Mutter — Mutter — Mutter! Zu neuen Qualen erwacht? O, das ist hart, bitterer als der Tod.

Papageno: Bin ich nicht ein Narr, dass ich mich schrecken liess? Es gibt ja schwarze Vögel in der Welt, warum denn nicht auch schwarze Menschen? Ah! Hier ist das schöne Fräulein noch. Du Tochter der nächtlichen Königin!

Pamina: Nächtliche Königin? Wer bist du?

Papageno: Ein Abgesandter der sternflammenden Königin.

Pamina: Meiner Mutter? O Wonne. Dein Name?

Papageno: Papageno.

Pamina: Papageno? Papageno—ich erinnere mich, den Namen oft gehört zu haben; dich selbst aber sah ich nie.

Papageno: Ich kam heute früh, wie gewöhnlich, zu deiner Mutter Palast mit meiner Lieferung. Eben als ich im Begriffe war, meine Vögel abzugeben, sah ich einen Menschen vor mir, der sich Prinz nennen lässt. Dieser Prinz hat deine Mutter so für sich eingenommen, dass sie ihm dein Bildnis schenkte und ihm befahl, dich zu befreien. Sein Entschluss war so schnell, als seine Liebe zu dir.

Pamina: Liebe? Er liebt mich also? O, sage mir das noch einmal; ich höre das Wort Liebe gar zu gern!

Papageno: Das glaub' ich dir; du bist ja ein Mädchen! Komm mit! du wirst Augen machen, wenn du den schönen Jüngling erblickst.

Pamina: Wohl denn, es sei gewagt! Aber wenn dies ein Fallstrick wäre—wenn dieser nun ein böser Geist von Sarastros Gefolge wäre?

Papageno: Ich ein böser Geist? Wo denkst du hin?

Pamina: Vergib, vergib, wenn ich dich beleidigt! Du hast ein gefühlvolles Herz; das sehe ich in jedem deiner Züge.

Papageno: Ach, freilich habe ich ein gefühlvolles Herz! Aber was nützt mir das alles? Ich möchte mir oft alle meine Federn ausrupfen, wenn ich bedenke, dass Papageno noch keine Papagena hat.

Pamina: Geduld, Freund! Der Himmel wird auch für dich sorgen; er wird dir eine Freundin schicken, ehe du dir's vermutest.

Nº 7. Duet

Andantino
PAMINA
The kind-ly voice of Mo - ther Na-ture Wakes love in
Bei Män-nern, wel - che Lie - be füh-len fehlt auch ein
p
Pam.
bird and beast and flower;
gu-tes Her-ze nicht.
PAPAGENO
There's not on earth a sin-gle creature That can re - sist that ten-der
Die süs-sen Trie-be mit-zu-füh-len, ist dann der Wei-ber er - ste
Pam.
The law of love let us.. then own, All life de-pends on love.. a - lone, all life de -
Wir wol-len uns der Lie - be weih'n, wir le-ben durch die Lieb' al-lein, wir le - ben
f
Pap.
power. The law of love let us then own, All life de-pends on love a - lone, all life de -
Pflicht. Wir wol-len uns der Lie - be weih'n, wir le-ben durch die Lieb' al-lein, wir le-ben
pp
mf
Pam.
-pends on love a - lone.
durch die Lieb' al - lein.
That joy... to
Die Lieb' ver -
Pap.
-pends on love a - lone.
durch die Lieb' al - lein.
p dolce

Pam.
Pap.
ev - 'ry crea - ture grant-ed Is felt.. no less.... by.. all...... man-kind;
-süs - set je - de Pla-ge, ihr op-fert je - de Kre - a - tur.
'Tis deep in
Sie wür-zet
The law.. of
Ihr ho - her
ev - 'ry soul.... im-plant-ed That each its kin - dred soul must find. The law of
uns - re Le - bens-ta - ge, sie wirkt im Krei - se der.... Na - tur. Ihr ho - her
love let us...... then own, All life de - pends on love.... a - lone, all life de -
Zweck zeigt deut - lich an, nichts ed - ler sei als Weib und Mann, nichts ed - ler
love let us then own, All life de - pends on love a - lone, all life de -
Zweck zeigt deut - lich an, nichts ed - ler sei als Weib und Mann, nichts ed - ler
-pends on love a - lone, life.... de-pends on love a -
sei als Weib und Mann. Mann und Weib, und Weib und
-pends on love a - lone, life.... de-pends on love a -
sei als Weib und Mann. Mann und Weib, und Weib und
p
f
pp
mf
dolce

sotto voce
f
sotto voce
Pam.
-lone. They that know the joys of love Rise to join the gods a-bove, They that
Mann, Mann und Weib, und Weib und Mann rei - chen an die Gott-heit an, Mann und
sotto voce
f
sotto voce
Pap.
-lone. They that know the joys of love Rise to join the gods a-bove, They that
Mann, Mann und Weib, und Weib und Mann rei - chen an die Gott-heit an, Mann und
f
p
f
Pam.
know the joys of love Rise to join the gods a - bove,
Weib, und Weib und Mann rei - chen an die Gott - heit an,
f
Pap.
know the joys of love Rise to join the gods a - bove,
Weib, und Weib und Mann rei - chen an die Gott - heit an,
f
p
fp
Pam.
the gods a - bove, the gods a - bove.
die Gott-heit an, die Gott-heit an.
Pap.
join the gods a-bove, join the gods a - bove.
an die Gott-heit an, an die Gott-heit an.
fp
cresc.
f
p

Scene 3. A grove. At the back of the scene a Temple, over the portal of which are the words "Temple of Wisdom". A colonade of pillars leads to two other Temples, on one of which is inscribed "Temple of Reason", on the other "Temple of Nature."

Nº 8. Finale

Larghetto
TAMINO is led on by the THREE GENII.
p
mf

1st & 2nd GENII
Thus far we set thee on thy way; Fare forth a-lone, no dan-ger
Zum Zie - le führt dich die - se Bahn, doch musst du, Jüngling, männlich
3rd GENIUS
Thus far we set thee on thy way; Fare forth a-lone, no dan-ger
Zum Zie - le führt dich die - se Bahn, doch musst du, Jüngling, männlich
p

1. G.
2. G.
fear - ing. Yet e - ver this com-mand o-bey: Be si - lent, pa-tient, per-se-
sie - gen. Drum hö - re uns-re Leh-re an: Sei standhaft, duld-sam und ver-
3. G.
fear - ing. Yet e - ver this com-mand o-bey: Be si - lent, pa-tient, per-se-
sie - gen. Drum hö - re uns-re Leh-re an: Sei standhaft, duld-sam und ver-
ten.
ten.
ten.
ten.

1. G.
2. G.
3. G.
-ve-ring! Such
-schwiegen! Dies
TAMINO
Oh tell me, tell me, spi-rits three, If I may set Pa-mi-na free?
Ihr holden Kna-ben, sagt mir an, ob ich Pa-mi-na ret-ten kann?
ten.
words are not for us to say; Be si-lent, pa-tient, per-se-ve-ring! A
kund-zu-tun, steht uns nicht an; sei stand-haft, duld-sam und verschwiegen! Be-
man-ly part thou hast to play, If this the goal .... thou would'st be
-den-ke dies, kurz, sei ein Mann, dann, Jüngling, wirst .... du männ-lich
If this the goal thou would'st be
dann, Jüngling, wirst du männ-lich
near-ing, if this the goal .... thou would'st be near-ing.
sie-gen, dann, Jüngling, wirst .... du männ-lich sie-gen.
Exeunt.
mf

RECITATIVE
TAMINO
Oh may these mystic words of wis-dom Up-on my
Die Weis-heits-leh-re die-ser Kna-ben sei e-wig
p
heart be grav'd for e-ver. What is my fate? where am I now? O sure-ly, none but
mir ins Herz ge-gra-ben. Wo bin ich nun? Was wird aus mir? Ist dies der Sitz der
fp
gods dwell here. What words do I read there in-scrib'd on the gate-way?
Göt - ter hier? Es zei-gen die Pfor-ten, es zei-gen die Säu-len,
Allegro
"To Na-ture, to Rea-son, to Wis-dom, these tem-ples!" But who .... were the
dass Klugheit und Ar-beit und Kün-ste hier wei-len; wo Tä - - tig-keit
p
buil-ders that rais'd .... them so fair? Ah, sure no-thing e - vil could find har-bour
thro-net und Müs - - siggang weicht, er-hält sei-ne Herrschaft das La-ster nicht
f

Allegro assai
T.
there.
leicht.
Then scorning all dan-ger an en-trance I'll make;
Ich wa-ge mich mu-tig zur Pforte hin-ein;
f
f
T.
My pur-pose is no-ble, my ho-nour's at stake! ....
die Ab-sicht ist e-del und lau-ter und rein. ....
Thou vile se-du-cer,
Er-zitt-re, fei-ger
p
f
T.
trem-ble now!
Bö-se-wicht!
To save Pa-mi-na,
Pa-mi-na ret-ten,
to save Pa-mi-na
Pa-mi-na ret-ten
was my vow.
ist mir Pflicht.
f
f
He moves towards the right-hand entrance.
T.
Stand back? Stand
Zu-rück? Zu-
VOICES (behind)
f
Stand back!
Zu-rück!
p
f
f

He moves towards the left-hand entrance.
T.
back? I'll try my for-tune here.
rück? So wag' ich hier mein Glück.
VOICES (behind)
f
Stand back!
Zu-rück!
tr
p
f
V.
What? here too I'm re-puls'd? Yet, one door there still remains; Per-chance I'll find an entrance there.
Auch hier ruft man zu-rück? Da seh' ich noch ei-ne Tür'! Vielleicht find ich den Eingang hier.
Adagio
He is about to go up to the central door. A priest (the Orator) comes out of the temple.
PRIEST
What would'st thou here, au-da-cious youth? What seek'st in this our sanct-u-ary?
Wo willst du, küh-ner Fremdling, hin? Was suchst du hier im Hei-lig-tum?
I come by
Der Lieb' und
dolce

Andante a tempo
T.
right of Love and Truth.
Tu - gend Ei - gen - tum.
Pr.
Thy words ring no-ble to the ear; But say, what
Die Wor - te sind von ho - hem Sinn! Al - lein, wie
mfp
a tempo, Adagio
Pr.
right hast thou to speak them? Not Love nor Truth thy pas-sion guides, But Lies and
willst du die-se fin - den? Dich lei - tet Lieb' und Tu-gend nicht, weil Tod und
p
T.
Yes, ha-tred for a cru-el deed.
Nur Ra-che für den Bö-se-wicht!
Pr.
Ha - tred sent thee hi - ther.
Ra - che dich ent - zün - den.
We know no act or thought that's
Den wirst du wohl bei uns nicht
cresc.
f
p
(rapidly)
T.
This is the strong-hold of Sa - ras - tro.
Sa - ra - stro herrscht in die - sen Grün - den?
Pr.
cru - el.
fin - den.
'Tis true, Sa -
Ja, ja, Sa -

T.
Pr.
(rapidly)
Yet not in Wis-dom's ho-ly shrine?
Doch in dem Weisheits-tempel nicht?
Your wis-dom's
So ist denn
-ras-tro rules us here.
-ra-stro herrschet hier.
(slowly) Of all her sons the wis-est he.
Er herrscht im Weisheits-tempel hier.
fp
(going)
nought.... but vile de-ceit!
al - les Heu-che-lei!
Yes, let me go;
Ja, ich will gehn,
Wilt thou so soon be gone?
Willst du schon wieder gehn?
f
p
f
hate - ful place! Why did I e'er come here?
froh und frei, nie eu-re Tem-pel sehn!
Nay, tell me all thy mind; me-
Er-klär' dich nä-her mir, dich
p dolce
Sa - ras-tro rules you here; that sure-ly is e-nough.
Sa - ra-stro herr-schet hier, das ist mir schon ge-nug!
-thinks thou art de-ceiv'd.
täu-schet ein Be-trug.
fp
f
f
Ped.

T.
Pr.
There's none that I hate
Ich hass' ihn e-wig,
If life be dear to thee, speak fur-ther, go not hence. Sa-ras-tro dost thou hate?
Wenn du dein Le-ben liebst, so re-de, blei-be da! Sa-ra-stro has-sest du?
p
fp
Ped.
more.
ja!
Is he not cru-el past be-lief?
Er ist ein Unmensch, ein Ty-rann!
Why dost thou hate him? Tell me that.
So gieb mir dei-ne Gründe an!
What proof is
Ist das, was
p
f
f
A wo-man's tears may sure-ly prove it, Whom he has plung'd in end - less
Durch ein un-glück-lich Weib er-wie-sen, das Gram und Jam-mer nie - der-
there of that thou say-est?
du ge-sagt er-wie-sen?
p
woe.
-drückt.
A wo-man then has told thee this? 'Twas like a wo-man thus to talk, And like a
Ein Weib hat al- so dich be-rückt? Ein Weib tut we-nig, plaudert viel, du, Jüngling,

T.
Pr.
His
Die
boy to think it true. Wait till Sa-ra-stro show to thee The pur-pose of his ac-tion here.
glaubst dem Zun-gen-spiel? O, leg-te doch Sa-ra-stro dir die Ab-sicht sei-ner Handlung für!
pur-pose is but all too clear: Did he not snatch the fair Pa-mi-na By
Ab-sicht ist nur all-zu klar! Riss nicht der Räu-ber ohn' Er-bar-men Pa-
force from her un-hap-py mo-ther? Where is she?
-mi-na aus der Mut-ter Ar-men? Wo ist sie,
PRIEST
Yes, sure-ly, that I'll not de-ny.
Ja, Jüng-ling, was du sagst, ist wahr.
or am I too late? Was hers some doom I dare not name?
die man uns ge-raubt? Man op-fer-te viel-leicht sie schon?
My son, have
Dir dies zu

T.
Pr.
What means this
Er-klär' dies
pa-tience, wait a while; 'Tis yet too soon to ans-wer thee.
sa-gen, teu-rer Sohn, ist jetzt und mir noch nicht er-laubt.
rid-dle? speak the truth.
Rät-sel, täusch' mich nicht.
When wilt thou
Wann al-so
My tongue is bound by du-ty's oath.
Die Zun-ge bin-det Eid und Pflicht.
Andante a tempo
break the bond of si-lence?
wird die Dek-ke schwin-den?
When friend-ship leads thee by the hand To
So-bald dich führt der Freund-schaft Hand in's
O end-less night! hast thou no
O ew'-ge Nacht, wann wirst du
He goes back into the temple.
join the tem-ple's ho-ly band.
Hei-lig-tum zum ew'-gen Band.

T.
break-ing? When dawns the day mine eyes are seek-ing?
schwinden? Wann wird das Licht mein Au - ge fin-den?
sotto voce
Tenor
Soon, soon; courage,
Bald, bald, Jüngling,
VOICES (behind)
sotto voce
Bass
Soon, soon; courage,
Bald, bald, Jüngling,
T.
Light! light! yes, though it blind mine eyes. O tell me, voice of
Bald, bald, bald, sagt ihr, o - der nie? Ihr Un-sicht-ba - ren,
V.
seek the light!
o - der nie!
seek the light!
o - der nie!
f
T.
mys-te-ry, Lives then Pa-mi-na still?
sa-get mir, lebt denn Pa-mi-na noch?
sotto voce
Pa-mi - na, Pa-mi - na
Pa-mi - na, Pa-mi - na
V.
sotto voce
Pa-mi - na, Pa-mi - na
Pa-mi - na, Pa-mi - na
fp
80

T.
She lives? she lives? I thank you for that word.
Sie lebt? sie lebt? Ich dan - ke euch da für!
V.
still doth live.
le - bet noch.
still doth live.
le - bet noch.
f
T.
Oh that my tongue could on-ly ut - ter, Ye gods a-bove, my grateful rap-ture; Pa -
O wenn ich doch im Stan-de wä - re, All-mäch-ti - ge, zu eu-rer Eh - re mit
T.
He takes his flute
-mi - na lives! shall I not soon be hold her? Yes, for her all I'll en-dure!
je - dem To - ne mei-nen Dank zu schildern, wie er hier, hier..... ent-sprang.
p
f
Andante
and plays. All sorts of wild animals come and listen to him.
Fl.

TAMINO
O... voice of... ma - gic me - lo - dy! O.... strain....... en - thral - ling! Se -
Wie stark ist... nicht dein Zau - ber-ton, weil, hol - - de Flö - te, hol-de
T.
(plays)
- re - ner thoughts... thou wak'st in.. me, My.. soul to loft-ier pur - pose call - ing.
Flö - te,.. durch...... dein Spie - len selbst wil-de Tie-re Freu-de... füh - len!
(plays)
Wild na - ture's child-ren... own thy charm,
Wie stark ist... nicht dein Zau - ber-ton,
And flock a - round, their haunts de - sert - ing; The...
weil, hol-de Flö - te,.. durch dein Spie - len, hol-de
The animals gradually go away.
fierce lose all .... de - sire to... harm, The ti - mid fear no hurt-ing. Ah, but Pa-
Flö - te,.. durch...... dein Spie - len selbst wil - de Tie - re Freu - de_ Doch, nur Pa-
cresc.
mf
p

(plays)
T.
-mi-na, but Pa-mi-na's far a-way, but Pa-mi-na's far a-way;
-mi-na, nur Pa-mi-na bleibt da-von, nur Pa-mi-na bleibt da-von!
(plays)
Pa-mi-na, Pa-mi-na,
Pa-mi-na, Pa-mi-na,
(plays)
hear me, hear me play! In
hö-re, hö-re mich! Um-
(plays) (plays)
vain, in vain! Where, where, where, where shall I......
-sonst! um-sonst! Wo, wo, wo, ach wo, wo....
cresc.
PAPAGENO's pan-pipe is heard answering.
(plays)
find thee, say? Ah! a fa-mi-liar note I hear,
find' ich dich? Ha! das ist Pa-pa-ge-no's Ton.

(plays)
(PAPAGENO answers)
(plays)
(PAPAGENO answers)
Presto
T.
That tells me Pa-pa-ge-no's near. Per-
Viel-leicht sah er Pa-mi-na schon, viel-
pp
Adagio
Presto
-chance Pa-mi-na he has found, Per-chance, per - chance she hears the..ma-gic
-leicht sah er Pa-mi-na schon, viel-leicht, viel - leicht.. führt mich der..Ton zu
ff
p
-sound, she hears the.. ma-gic.. sound, Per-chance.. the..
ihr, führt mich der Ton zu ihr, führt mich..... der..
fp
He rushes off; PAPAGENO and PAMINA hurry on round the opposite corner.
flute will guide.......... my steps to her.
Ton, der Ton,............ der Ton zu ihr!
cresc.
f
p
Andante
PAMINA
Let us has-ten quick as thought, To es-cape be-fore we're caught; If we
Schnel-le Füs-se, ra-scher Mut schützt vor Fein - des List und Wut. Fän-den
PAPAGENO
Let us has-ten quick as thought, To es-cape be-fore we're caught; If we
Schnel-le Füs-se, ra-scher Mut schützt vor Fein - des List und Wut. Fän-den

Pam.
once the Prince can find, Then all our dan-ger, all our dan-ger's left be-hind. If we
wir Ta - mi - no doch, sonst er - wi-schen, sonst er - wi-schen sie uns noch, fänden
Pap.
once the Prince can find, Then all our dan-ger, all our dan-ger's left be-hind. If we
wir Ta - mi - no doch, sonst er - wi-schen, sonst er - wi-schen sie uns noch, fänden
sf p
Pam.
once the Prince can find, Then all our dan-ger, all our dan-ger's left be-hind.
wir Ta - mi - no doch, sonst er - wi-schen, sonst er-wi-schen sie uns noch!
Pap.
once the Prince can find, Then all our dan-ger, all our dan-ger's left be-hind.
wir Ta - mi - no doch, sonst er - wi-schen, sonst er-wi-schen sie uns noch!
sf p
Pam.
Oh, ... Ta - mi - no!
Hol - - - der Jüng - ling!
(He whistles)
Pap.
Hush, be si-lent! I know better how to call him.
Stil-le, stil-le, stil-le, stil-le! Ich kann's besser.
Pam.
(The Flute answers from behind)
Yes, the ma - gic flute gives
Wel-che Freu - de ist wohl
Pap.
Yes, the ma - gic flute gives
Wel-che Freu - de ist wohl

Pam.
an-swer, Yes, a-gain its notes I hear, Then Ta-mi-no must be near!......'Twas the
grösser, Freund Ta-mi-no hört uns schon; hie-her kam sein Flö-ten-ton!........Welch'ein
Pap.
an-swer, Yes, a-gain its notes I hear, Then Ta-mi-no must be near!......'Twas the
grösser, Freund Ta-mi-no hört uns schon; hie-her kam sein Flö-ten-ton!........Welch'ein
cresc.
f
p
Pam.
su-rest way to... greet him; Let us has-ten, let us has-ten on to meet him, 'Twas the
Glück, wenn ich.. ihn.. fin-de! Nur ge-schwinde, nur ge-schwinde, nur ge-schwinde! Welch'ein
Pap.
su-rest way to... greet him; Let us has-ten, let us has-ten on to meet him, 'Twas the
Glück, wenn ich.. ihn.. fin-de! Nur ge-schwinde, nur ge-schwinde, nur ge-schwinde! Welch'ein
sf p
Pam.
su-rest way.. to.... greet him, Let us.... has-ten, let us... has-ten, let us..
Glück, wenn ich... ihn.. fin-de! Nur ge-schwinde, nur ge-schwinde, nur ge-
Pap.
su-rest way.. to.... greet him, Let us.... has-ten, let us... has-ten, let us..
Glück, wenn ich... ihn... fin-de! Nur ge-schwinde, nur ge-schwinde, nur ge-
sf p sf p sf p
They run off, but are intercepted and driven back by MONOSTATOS.
Pam.
has-ten, let us has-ten, let us has-ten, let us has-ten on to meet him!
-schwinde, nur ge-schwinde, nur ge-schwinde, nur ge-schwinde, nur ge-schwinde!
MONOSTATOS
Let us has-ten, let us has-ten on to
Nur ge-schwinde, nur ge-schwinde, nur ge-
Pap.
has-ten, let us has-ten, let us has-ten, let us has-ten on to meet him!
-schwinde, nur ge-schwinde, nur ge-schwinde, nur ge-schwinde, nur ge-schwinde!

Allegro
M.
meet him! Ha! caught in the ve - ry act! So you thought you could es-
-schwinde! Ha! hab' ich euch noch er-wischt! Nur her - bei mit Stahl und
f
sfp
M.
-cape me! I'll teach you to dis-o- bey me, I'll teach you to dis-o-bey me! With Mo-
Ei - sen! Wart, ich will euch Mo-res weisen, Mo-res wei-sen, Mo-res wei-sen! Den Mo-
f
sfp
f
M.
-no - sta-tos to tri-fle! Ne'er a-gain shall you de-fy me! Come, ye slaves, and bind them
-no - sta-tos be - rük-ken! Nur her-bei mit Band und Stricken! He, ihr Skla-ven, kommt her-
sfp
f
p
f
p
PAMINA
All our fair - est hopes are past.
Ach, nun ist's mit uns vor-bei!
Enter Slaves with chains.
M.
fast.
-bei!
Slaves, I say! come, bind them fast!
He, ihr Skla-ven, kommt her - bei!
PAPAGENO
All our fair - est hopes are past.
Ach, nun ist's mit uns vor-bei!
Just a
Wer viel
f
p

Pap.
chance, just a chance, just a chance I still can see; Here's the thing to set us
wagt, wer viel wagt, wer viel wagt, ge-winnt oft viel. Komm, du schö-nes Glok-ken-
Pap.
He plays
free. Set the ma-gic bells a-ring-ing; Help to us they may be bringing.
-spiel, lass die Glöckchen klin-gen, klin-gen, dass die Oh-ren ih-nen sin-gen!
8
on the bells. MONOSTATOS and the Slaves are startled and drop the chains; they begin to sing, and dance off grotesquely.
8
Tenor I
Tenor II
CHORUS
Bass
O... lis-ten, what is it that tin-kles so clear? La-ra-la la la
Das klin-get so herr-lich, das klin-get so schön! La-ra-la la la
O lis-ten, what is it that tin-kles so clear? La-ra-la la la
Das klin-get so herr-lich, das klin-get so schön! La-ra-la la la
8
Ch.
la-ra-la, la la la-ra-la! 'Tis something I ne-ver did see nor did
la-ra-la, la la la-ra-la! Nie hab' ich so et-was ge-hört, noch ge-
la-ra-la, la la la-ra-la! 'Tis something I ne-ver did see nor did
la-ra-la, la la la-ra-la! Nie hab' ich so et-was ge-hört, noch ge-
8

Ch.
hear. La-ra-la la la la - ra-la la la, la - ra - la! 'Tis something I ne-ver did
-sehn. La-ra-la la la la - ra-la la la, la - ra - la! Nie hab' ich so et-was ge -
hear. La-ra-la la la la - ra-la la la, la - ra - la! 'Tis something I ne-ver did
-sehn. La-ra-la la la la - ra-la la la, la - ra - la! Nie hab' ich so et-was ge -
Ch.
see nor did hear. La-ra-la la la la - ra-la la la, la - ra - la!
-hört, noch ge-sehn. La-ra-la la la la ra-la la la, la - ra - la!
see nor did hear. La-ra-la la la la - ra-la la la, la - ra - la!
-hört, noch ge-sehn. La-ra-la la la la - ra-la la la, la - ra - la!
PAMINO
When the ma-gic bells are heard Chimes of mu - sic wa - king, Wrath for-gets his an-gry word,
Könn-te je-der bra-ve Mann sol - che Glöckchen fin - den, sei - ne Fein-de würden dann
PAPAGENO
When the ma-gic bells are heard Chimes of mu - sic wa - king, Wrath for-gets his an-gry word,
Könn-te je-der bra-ve Mann sol - che Glöckchen fin - den, sei - ne Fein-de würden dann
mf
p
Pam.
Frowns to smiles are breaking. Thus our foes to friends we turn; Thus to laugh we make them learn,
oh - ne Mü - he schwinden. Und er leb-te oh - ne sie in der be-sten Har-mo - nie,
Pap.
Frowns to smiles are breaking. Thus our foes to friends we turn; Thus to laugh we
oh - ne Mü - he schwinden. Und er leb - te oh - ne sie in der be-sten

Pam.
thus to laugh, to laugh we... make them learn. Make them laugh and make them sing;
in der be - sten, be - sten Har - mo - nie. Nur der Freundschaft Har - mo - nie
Pap.
make them learn, thus to laugh we make them learn. Make them laugh and make them sing;
Har - mo - nie, in der be - sten Har - mo - nie. Nur der Freundschaft Har - mo - nie
mf
Pam.
Friend-ship fol - lows af - ter; So to ev-'ry man we bring Mu-sic, friend-ship, laughter!
mil - dert die Be - schwerden; oh - ne die - se Sym-pa-thie ist kein Glück auf Er - den.
Pap.
Friend-ship fol - lows af - ter; So to ev-'ry man we bring Mu-sic, friend-ship, laughter!
mil - dert die Be - schwerden; oh - ne die - se Sympa - thie ist kein Glück auf Er - den.
p
mf
p
Allegro maestoso
PAPAGENO
What means all that shouting? some
Was soll das be - deu-ten? Ich
A flourish of trumpets. The Chorus are heard singing behind.
Soprano
Contralto
All hail to Sara-stro! we bend be-fore him!
Es le - be Sara-stro! Sa - ra-stro le - be!
CHORUS
Tenor
Bass
All hail to Sara-stro! we bend be-fore him!
Es le - be Sara-stro! Sa - ra-stro le - be!
Allegro maestoso
f
p
tr

82

PAMINA
Oh friend, no hope in - deed remains; It means that great Sa-rastro comes.
O Freund, nun ist's um uns ge - tan; dies kün - det den Sa-rastro an.
Pap.
danger approaches!
zitt're, ich be - be!
I
O
Pap.
wish I were a mouse With - in some cran-ny hi-ding, Or like a snail were sli-ding In -
wär' ich ei - ne Maus, wie würd' ich mich verstecken! Wär' ich so klein wie Schnecken, so
PAMINA
The truth, friend! the
Die Wahr - heit! die
Pap.
-to my lit-tle house! But say, what ans-wer can we give him?
kröch' ich in mein Haus! Mein Kind, was wer-den wir nun sprechen?
Enter Priests and People, followed by SARASTRO and Attendants.
Pam.
truth, friend! ne'er would I deceive him.
Wahr - heit! wär' sie auch Verbrechen.
f
tr

All hail to Sara-stro! we bend low before him, With heartfelt de-vo - tion and
Es le - be Sara-stro! Sa - ra-stro soll le - ben! Er ist es, dem wir uns mit
CHORUS
All hail to Sara-stro! we bend low before him, With heartfelt de-vo - tion and
Es le - be Sara-stro! Sa - ra-stro soll le - ben! Er ist es, dem wir uns mit
All hail to Sara-stro! we bend low before him, With heartfelt de-vo - tion and
Es le - be Sara-stro! Sa - ra-stro soll le - ben! Er ist es, dem wir uns mit
All hail to Sara-stro! we bend low before him, With heartfelt de-vo - tion and
Es le - be Sara-stro! Sa - ra-stro soll le - ben! Er ist es, dem wir uns mit
tr
tr
p
love we a-dore him. 'Tis his.. lo-ving wis-dom that guides us a - right, 'tis
Freu-den er-ge - ben! Stets mög' er des Le-bens als Wei - ser sich freun, stets
p
Ch.
love we a-dore him. 'Tis his lo-ving wis-dom
Freu-den er-ge - ben! Stets mög' er des Le-bens
p
love we a-dore him. 'Tis his lo-ving wis-dom that guides us a - right, 'tis
Freu-den er-ge - ben! Stets mög' er des Le-bens als Wei - ser sich freun, stets
p
love we a-dore him. 'Tis his lo-ving wis-dom
Freu-den er-ge - ben! Stets mög' er des Le-bens
p

f
his loving wisdom that guides us aright, Then lead us, Sarastro, to truth and to light, then
mög'er des Lebens als Weisersichfreun! Er ist unser Abgott, dem Alle sich weih'n, er
that guides us aright, Then lead us, Sarastro, to truth and to light, then
als Weisersichfreun! Er ist unser Abgott, dem Alle sich weih'n, er
Ch.
lead us, Sarastro, to truth and to light, to truth and to light, to truth and to light!
ist unser Abgott, dem Alle sich weih'n, dem Alle sich weih'n, dem Alle sich weih'n!

Larghetto
PAMINA throws herself at SARASTRO's feet.
Sir, let me all con-fess to thee: I broke thy law and sought es-
Herr, ich bin zwar Ver-bre-cherin, ich woll - te dei-ner Macht ent-
f
p
Pam.
-cape. But yet not all the fault was mine; The wicked Moor with love pur-
-flieh'n. Al-lein die Schuld lag nicht an mir; der bö-se Mohr ver-lang-te
Pam.
-sued me: That was the cause for which I fled.
Lie - be; da-rum, o Herr, ent-floh ich dir.
SARASTRO
A-rise and dry thy tears, Pa-
Steh auf, er- heit - re dich, o
S.
-mi - na, Dear child, thou hast no need to tell me; I know the se-crets of thy
Lie - be, denn oh - ne erst in dich zu drin-gen, weiss ich von deinem Herzen
p

S.
heart; I know to whom thy love is... giv'n, yes, to
mehr: du lie - best ei - nen an - dern sehr, ei - nen
S.
whom 'tis giv'n. Fear not, to love I'll ne'er com - pel thee; Yet 'tis too soon to set.. thee
an - dern sehr. Zur Lie - be will ich dich nicht zwin - gen, doch geb' ich dir die Frei - heit
S.
free, Fear not, to love I'll ne'er com - pel thee; Yet, yet 'tis too soon to set thee
nicht, zur Lie - be will ich dich nicht zwingen, doch, doch geb' ich dir die Frei - heit
PAMINA
I hear a voice.............. that calls me hence: It is my
Mich ru - fet ja.................... die Kin - des - pficht, denn mei - ne
S.
free.
nicht.
p

Pam.
S.
mo-ther's
Mut-ter
Think of her no more. Thy life were wreck'd for e - ver-more If I to her should once re-
steht in meiner Macht. Du würdest um dein Glück ge-bracht, wenn ich dich ih - ren Hän-den
mfp
cresc.
How could I... e'er for-get my mo-ther? She loves.. me, she
Mir klingt der Mut-ter-na-me süs-se! Sie ist..... es, sie
sign thee.
lies-se.
f
p
loves me
ist.... es
Name her not to me. A man to guide thy steps thou
und ein stol-zes Weib! Ein Mann muss eu - re Her - zen
mfp
f
fp
need-est, Since ne'er a - lone can wo-man find The hid-den road that leads to wis-dom.
lei - ten, denn oh - ne ihn pflegt je-des Weib aus sei-nem Wir-kungskreis zu schreiten.
f

Enter MONOSTATOS dragging on TAMINO.
Allegro
MONOSTATOS
So please your high - ness, come this
Nun stol - zer Jüng - ling nur hie -
p
TAMINO and PAMINA rush into each other's arms.
PAMINA
At last! My
Er ist's! Ich
TAMINO
At last!
Sie ist's!
M.
way; Per-haps Sa - ras - tro thou'lt o - bey.
- her! Hier ist Sa - ra - stro, un - ser Herr.
Pam.
love, 'tis he! At last! At last I
glaub' es kaum! Er ist's! Es schling' mein
T.
At last! My love, 'tis she!
Sie ist's! Es ist kein Traum!
Pam.
see thee face to face, And fold thee in my fond em-
Arm sich um ihn her, und wenn es auch mein En - de
T.
At last I see thee face to face, And fold thee in my fond em-
Es schling' mein Arm sich um sie her, und wenn es auch mein En - de

Pam.
brace.
wär'!
T.
brace.
wär'!
MONOSTATOS separates TAMINO and PAMINA
Ha! what ef - fron - te - ry! 'Tis past en -
Welch' ei - ne Drei - stig - keit! Gleich aus - ein -
f
Who is the stran - ger?
Was soll das heis - sen?
CHORUS
f
Who is the stran - ger?
Was soll das heis - sen?
f p f p
91
M.
kneeling to SARASTRO
- du - rance, as you shall learn.
- an - der! Das geht zu weit!
f p mfp
M.
Be - hold thy slave be - fore thee kneel - ing, A vile con - spi - ra - cy re -
Dein Skla - ve liegt zu dei - nen Füs - sen, lass'den ver - weg - nen Frev - ler
M.
veal - ing; Was e - ver tale so shame - less heard? The wretches there_ one's half a...
büs - sen! Be - denk, wie frech der Kna - be ist! Durch die - ses selt' - nen Vo - gels
fp fp fp fp

M.
bird—Had made a plot to steal Pa - mi-na And run a-way, had I not
List wollt' er Pa - mi - na dir ent - füh-ren, al-lein ich wusst' ihn aus - zu-
fp fp fp fp
M.
seen her. Thou know'st me, know's't my watch - ful
-spü - ren. Du kennst mich, mei - ne Wach - sam-
M.
eye—
-keit—
SARASTRO
As thou de-serv'st I rate thee high.
ver-dient, dass man ihr Lor - beer streut!
M.
Too gen-'rous art thou to thy
Schon dei - ne Gna - de macht mich
S.
Thy due re - ward thou now shalt have.
He, gebt dem Eh - ren-mann so - gleich—

M.
slave.
reich!
Not
Ach
S.
Then taste a sound bas-ti-na-do, knave!
nur sie-benund-sie-ben-zig Soh-len-streich'!
M.
that, not that I hoped, my gra-cious lord.
Herr, ach Herr, den Lohn er-hofft ich nicht.
S.
E-nough! it is thy due re-
Nicht Dank, es ist ja mei-ne
MONOSTATOS is led away by slaves.
S.
-ward.
Pflicht.
sotto voce
to the wisest of sages. with
We hail thee, Sa-ras-tro, of sa-ges the wis-est; The
CHORUS
Es le-be Sa-ra-stro, der gött-li-che Wei-se! Er
f
p

justice remembered throughout all the ages.
Ch.
just thou pro-tect-est, the un-just chas-tis-est.
loh-net und stra-fet in ähn-li-chem Krei-se.
just thou pro-tect-est, the un-just chas-tis-est.
loh-net und stra-fet in ähn-li-chem Krei-se.
SARASTRO
We bid these strangers wel-come here, If they our ho-ly life would know;
Führt die-se bei-den Fremd-lin-ge in un-sern Prü-fungs-tem-pel ein;
fp
Adagio, a tempo
S.
Place then the veil up-on their heads, They must pro-ba-tion un-der-go.
be-dek-ket ih-re Häup-ter dann, sie müs-sen erst ge-rei-nigt sein.
TAMINO and PAPAGENO are veiled by two Priests and conducted into the lower temple.
Presto
CHORUS
Sa-ras-tro! lead us on, we pray, The truth to
Wenn Tu-gend und Ge-rech-tig-keit der Gros-sen
Sa-ras-tro! lead us on, we pray, The truth to
Wenn Tu-gend und Ge-rech-tig-keit der Gros-sen

Ch.
seek with o - pen eyes, the truth to seek with o - pen eyes, the truth to seek with o - pen
Pfad mit Ruhm be-streut, der Gros-sen Pfad mit Ruhm be-streut, mit Ruhm be-streut, mit Ruhm be -
seek with o - pen eyes, the truth to seek with o - pen eyes, the truth to seek with o - pen
Pfad mit Ruhm be-streut, der Gros-sen Pfad mit Ruhm be-streut, mit Ruhm be-streut, mit Ruhm be -
'Tis Na - ture first that points the way,
dann ist die Erd' ein Him - - mel - reich,
Ch.
eyes; 'Tis Na-ture first that points the way,
-streut, dann ist die Erd' ein Him-mel-reich,
eyes; 'Tis Na-ture first that points the way, Then Rea - son's
-streut, dann ist die Erd' ein Him - mel - reich, dann ist die
Ch.
Then Rea-son's laws we must o - bey, then Rea-son's laws we must o - bey,
dann ist die Erd' ein Him-mel-reich und Sterb-li - che den Göt-tern gleich,
laws we must o - bey, then Rea-son's laws we must o - bey,
Erd' ein Him - - mel-reich und Sterb-li - che den Göt-tern gleich,

Ch.
Thus Wis - dom on our souls shall rise. So
und Sterb - li - che den Göt - tern gleich, dann
Thus Wis - dom on our souls shall rise. So
und Sterb - li - che den Göt - tern gleich, dann
Ch.
cast we off the shades of night, And e - ver strive to seek the
ist die Erd' ein Him - mel - reich und Sterb - li - che den Göt - tern
cast we off the shades of night, And e - ver strive to seek the
ist die Erd' ein Him - mel - reich und Sterb - li - che den Göt - tern
Ch.
light, So cast we off the shades of night, And
gleich, dann ist die Erd' ein Him - mel - reich und
light, So cast we off the shades of night, And
gleich, dann ist die Erd' ein Him - mel - reich und
Ch.
e - ver strive to seek the light, so strive .... we to
Sterb - li - che den Göt - tern gleich, den Göt - - - tern, den
e - ver strive to seek the light, so strive .... we to
Sterb - li - che den Göt - tern gleich, den Göt - - - tern, den

Ch.
seek the light, so strive.................. we to seek the
Göt - tern gleich, den Göt - - - tern, den Göt - tern
seek the light, so strive.................. we to seek the
Göt - tern gleich, den Göt - - - tern, den Göt - tern
Ch.
light, to seek the light, to seek the light,
gleich, den Göt - tern gleich, den Göt - tern gleich,
light, to seek the light, to seek the light,
gleich, den Göt - tern gleich, den Göt - tern gleich,
SARASTRO leads PAMINA into the temple.
Ch.
to seek the light.
den Göt - - tern gleich.
to seek the light.
den Göt - - tern gleich.
End of Act I

ACT II

Scene 1. A Grove of Palms.

enter SL

No. 9. March

Enter the priests, carrying trumpets, followed by SARASTRO.

'wander across SR meeting people

Sarastro: Brother initiates of the holy mysteries, I have called you here that you may prepare to receive a newcomer. The Prince Tamino waits at the northern gate of our temple, full of virtuous desire for that which we, too, have sought with toil and patience. Let it be our duty to watch over him, and hold out to him the hand of friendship.

1st Priest: Is he virtuous?

Sarastro: He is virtuous.

2nd Priest: Can he be silent?

Sarastro: He can.

3rd Priest: Does he love his fellow men?

Sarastro: Yes. If you account him worthy, give the sign.

Sarastro: Ihr in dem Weisheitstempel eingeweihten Diener der grossen Götter Osiris und Isis! Mit reiner Seele erklär' ich euch, dass unsere heutige Versammlung eine der wichtigsten unserer Zeit ist. Tamino, ein Königssohn, wandelt an der nördlichen Pforte unseres Tempels und seufzt mit tugendvollem Herzen nach einem Gegenstande, den wir alle mit Mühe und Fleiss erringen müssen. Diesen Tugendhaften zu bewachen, ihm freundschaftlich die Hand zu bieten, sei heute eine unserer wichtigsten Pflichten.

1. *Priester:* Er besitzt Tugend?

Sarastro: Tugend!

2. *Priester:* Auch Verschwiegenheit?

Sarastro: Verschwiegenheit.

3. *Priester:* Ist wohtätig?

Sarastro: Wohltätig! Haltet ihr ihn für würdig, so folgt meinem Beispiele.

 (The Priests blow their trumpets.) *(Die Priester blasen dreimal in die Hörner.)*

No. 9a

Adagio
f

Sarastro: For him have the gods chosen out the gentle and virtuous Pamina; it was for that reason that I removed her by force from her mother's keeping. That evil woman vaunts her power; she thinks to dazzle and delude the people with her degraded superstitions, and utterly to destroy this our temple of Nature, Reason and Wisdom. Shall she accomplish this? No! Let Tamino then be initiated into our mysteries, and united with her daughter Pamina, that they may disperse the darkness of superstition, and uphold with us the cause of truth and light.

(The Priests blow their trumpets.)

1st *Priest:* Great Sarastro, we hear thy words of wisdom, and revere them. Yet will Tamino have strength to endure the ordeals that await him? Remember, he is of royal blood.

Sarastro: He is a man; that is enough.

1st *Priest:* He is young; what if he pay for his initiation with his death?

Sarastro: He will be in the hands of Osiris and Isis, and will know the joys of the gods sooner than we ourselves.

(The Priests blow their trumpets.)

Sarastro: Lead Tamino and his companion into the forecourt of the temple. And thou, friend (*to the Orator*), fulfil thy sacred duty, and teach them the way of wisdom.

Sarastro: Pamina, das sanfte, tugendhafte Mädchen haben die Götter dem holden Jüngling bestimmt; dies ist der Grund, warum ich sie der stolzen Mutter entriss. Das Weib dünkt sich gross, hofft durch Blendwerk und Aberglauben das Volk zu berücken und unsern festen Tempelbau zu zerstören. Allein das soll sie nicht! Tamino selbst soll ihn mit uns befestigen und als Eingeweihter der Tugend Lohn, dem Laster aber Strafe sein.

(Die Priester blasen dreimal in die Hörner.)

1. *Priester:* Grosser Sarastro, deine weisheitsvollen Reden erkennen und bewundern wir; allein, wird Tamino auch die harten Prüfungen, so seiner warten, bestehen? Er ist Prinz.

Sarastro: Noch mehr—er ist Mensch!

1. *Priester:* Wenn er nun aber in seiner frühen Jugend leblos erblasste?

Sarastro: Dann ist er Osiris und Isis gegeben und wird der Götter Freuden früher fühlen als wir.

(Die Priester blasen dreimal in die Hörner.)

Sarastro: Man führe Tamino mit seinem Reisegefährten in den Vorhof des Tempels ein. Und du, Freund, vollziehe dein heiliges Amt und lehre durch deine Weisheit beide, was Pflicht der Menschheit sei, lehre sie die Macht der Götter erkennen!

No. 10 Aria

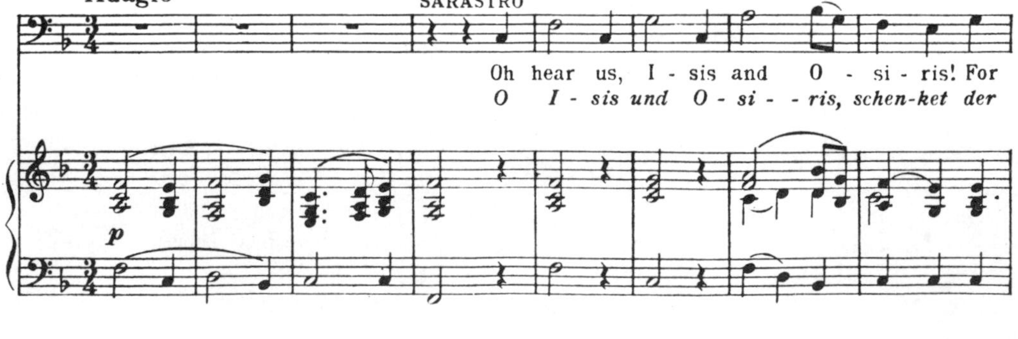
Adagio
SARASTRO
Oh hear us, I - sis and O - si - ris! For
O I - sis und O - si - - ris, schen-ket der
p

S.
these that seek your light we pray, In all their pe - - rils grant them pa-tience,
Weis-heit Geist dem neu-en Paar! Die ihr der Wand'-rer Schrit-te len-ket,
S.
And lead them safe in.. wis-dom's way,... And lead them safe in wis-dom's way.
stärkt mit Ge-duld sie in Ge-fahr,... stärkt mit Ge-duld sie in Ge-fahr.
S.
Let them draw near with-out de-
Lasst sie der Prü-fung Früch-te
Tenor I II
p
Oh lead them safe.... in wis-dom's way!
Stärkt mit Ge-duld sie in Ge-fahr!
Bass I II
p
Oh lead them safe... in wis-dom's way!
Stärkt mit Ge-duld sie in Ge-fahr!
Ped.
S.
-ni-al; Or if too frail to stand their tri-al, Their youth-ful ar-dour call... to
se-hen; doch soll-ten sie zu Gra-be ge-hen, so lohnt der Tu-gend küh-nen

Scene 2. Porch of the Temple.

(*Stage dark. Enter Tamino, followed by Papageno. Distant thunder.*)

Tamino: What a horrible night! Papageno, are you there?

Papageno: To be sure I am.

Tamino: Where are we now, I wonder?

Papageno: Where? If it were not so dark I might be able to tell you. (*Thunder.*) Oh—oh!

Tamino: Are you afraid?

Papageno: No—not afraid—but I feel a shiver all down my back. (*Thunder.*) Oh—oh!

Tamino: What ails you?

Papageno: I think it's a fever coming on.

Tamino: For shame, Papageno, be a man. (*Thunder.*)

Papageno: Oh-oh-oh!

(*Enter Two Priests, with lights.*)

Tamino: Eine schreckliche Nacht! Papageno, bist du noch bei mir?

Papageno: I, freilich!

Tamino: Wo denkst du, dass wir uns nun befinden?

Papageno: Wo? Ja, wenn's nicht finster wäre, wollt' ich dir's sagen—aber so. (*Donnerschlag.*) O weh!

Tamino: Du hast Furcht, wie ich höre.

Papageno: Furcht eben nicht, nur eiskalt läuft's mir über den Rücken. (*Donnerschlag.*) O weh!

Tamino: Was soll's?

Papageno: Ich glaube, ich bekomme ein kleines Fieber.

Tamino: Pfui, Papageno! Sei ein Mann!

Papageno: Ich wollt', ich wär ein Mädchen! (*Donnerschlag.*) O! O! O!

1st Priest: Ye strangers, what has led you to penetrate within our walls? What is it that you seek of us?

Tamino: Friendship and love.

1st Priest (to Tamino): Art thou ready to fight for these with thy life?

Tamino: Yes.

1st Priest: Even to die in the attempt?

Tamino: Yes.

1st Priest: Prince, there is yet time to turn back. One step farther and it is too late.

Tamino: I seek the goal of wisdom, and may Pamina's love be my reward.

1st Priest: Thou wilt submit to every ordeal?

Tamino: Yes, to all.

1st Priest: Thy hand upon it!

2nd Priest (to Papageno): And wouldst thou also seek the goal of wisdom?

Papageno: Wisdom? No; I'm a child of nature. All I want is to eat, drink and sleep—and if I could find a little wife, too——

2nd Priest: That thou wilt never obtain, unless thou submit to our ordeals, and art ready to risk thy life.

Papageno: Then I'll remain single.

2nd Priest: But if Sarastro had chosen a wife for thee, young and fair, feathered like thyself?

Papageno: What is her name?

2nd Priest: Papagena.

Papageno: Pa—Papagena? Well, I should like to have a sight of her.

2nd Priest: So thou shalt.

Papageno: But when I have seen her, shall I have to die? (*The Priest makes an ambiguous gesture.*) No, I'll remain single.

2nd Priest: Thou shalt see her; but thou must speak never a word with her until the appointed time. Canst hold thy peace so long?

Papageno: Ay, that I can.

2nd Priest: Thy hand upon it.

1st Priest (to Tamino): Prince, the same law of silence is laid upon thee. Thou shalt see Pamina, but thou shalt not speak with her, or with any woman. (*To both.*) This is the beginning of your probation.

1. *Priester:* Ihr Fremdlinge, was sucht oder fordert ihr von uns? Was treibt euch an, in unsere Mauern zu dringen?

Tamino: Freundschaft und Liebe.

1. *Priester:* Bist du bereit, sie mit deinem Leben zu erkämpfen?

Tamino: Ja!

1. *Priester:* Auch wenn Tod dein Los wäre?

Tamino: Ja!

1. *Priester:* Prinz, noch ist's Zeit zu weichen—einen Schritt weiter, und es ist zu spät.

Tamino: Weisheitslehre sei mein Sieg; Pamina, das holde Mädchen, mein Lohn!

1. *Priester:* Du unterziehst dich jeder Prüfung?

Tamino: Jeder!

1. *Priester:* Reiche mir deine Hand!

2. *Priester:* Willst auch du dir Weisheitsliebe erkämpfen?

Papageno: Kämpfen ist meine Sache nicht. Ich verlange auch im Grunde gar keine Weisheit. Ich bin so ein Naturmensch, der sich mit Schlaf, Speise und Trank begnügt; und wenn es ja sein könnte, dass ich mir einmal ein schönes Weibchen fange——

2. *Priester:* Das wirst du nie erhalten, wenn du dich nicht unseren Prüfungen unterziehst.

Papageno: Worin besteht diese Prüfung?

2. *Priester:* Dich allen unseren Gesetzen zu unterwerfen, selbst den Tod nicht zu scheuen.

Papageno: Ich bleibe ledig!

2. *Priester:* Wenn nun aber Sarastro dir ein Mädchen aufbewahrt hätte, jung und schön, das an Farbe und Kleidung dir ganz gleich wäre?

Papageno: Und heisst?

2. *Priester:* Papagena.

Papageno: Wie? Pa—Papagena? Die möcht' ich aus blosser Neugierde sehen.

2. *Priester:* Sehen kannst du sie!

Papageno: Aber wenn ich sie gesehen habe, hernach muss ich sterben? Ich bleibe ledig!

2. *Priester:* Sehen kannst du sie, aber bis zur verlaufenen Zeit kein Wort mit ihr sprechen. Wird dein Geist so viel Standhaftigkeit besitzen, deine Zunge in Schranken zu halten?

Papageno: O ja!

2. *Priester:* Deine Hand!

1. *Priester:* Auch dir, Prinz, legen die Götter ein heilsames Stillschweigen auf. Du wirst Pamina sehen, aber nicht sie sprechen dürfen; dies ist der Anfang eurer Prüfungszeit.

Nº 11 Duet

Andante
1st PRIEST
Be-ware the wiles of wo - - man's weav-ing, Would ye be
Be-wah-ret euch vor Wei - ber - tük - ken, dies ist des
2nd PRIEST
Be-ware the wiles of wo - - man's weav - ing, Would ye be
Be-wah-ret euch vor Wei - - ber - tük - ken, dies ist des
p
1st Pr.
worth - y of... this place;... Too ma - ny yield to their de - ceiv-ing, And,
Bun - des er - ste Pflicht! Manch' wei-ser Mann liess sich be - rük-ken, er
2nd Pr.
worth - y of this place; Too ma - ny yield to their de - ceiv - ing, And,
Bun - des er - ste Pflicht! Manch' wei-ser Mann liess sich be - rük-ken, er
1st Pr.
care - less, and, care - less, fall from wis - dom's grace. At
fehl - te, er fehl - te und ver - sah sich's nicht. Ver -
2nd Pr.
care - less, and, care - less, fall from wis - dom's grace. At
fehl - te, er fehl - te und ver - sah sich's nicht. Ver -

Papageno: Ho there! Bring lights, bring lights! Why are we always left in darkness?

Tamino: Bear thy trial with patience. Remember, it is the will of the gods.

Papageno: He! Lichter her! Das ist doch wunderlich: so oft einen die Herren verlassen, so sieht man mit offenen Augen nichts.

Tamino: Ertrag' es mit Geduld und denke, es ist der Götter Wille.

Nº 12 Quintet

T.
wo - man to be speak-ing?
Wei - bern hier zu spre-chen?
Hush, I tell thee, speak no
Stil - le sag' ich, schwei-ge
Pap.
For us some dread-ful fate's in store.
Du hörst ja, wir sind Bei-de hin!
fp
fp
f
p
1st & 2nd LADIES
The Queen knows
Ganz nah ist
T
more.
still!
Pap.
Hush in - deed, and speak no more! Was ev-er man so plagu'd be - fore?
Im-mer still, und im-mer still, und im-mer still, und im-mer still!
cresc.
f
p
1. L.
2. L.
all and yet... may save, But not if you her... an - ger brave.
euch die.. Kö - ni - gin, sie drang im Tem-pel heim-lich ein.
3rd LADY
The Queen may save, But.. not... if.... you her an - ger brave.
Die Kö - ni - gin, sie...drang im... Tem-pel heim - lich ein.
PAPAGENO
The
Wie?
tr
tr

TAMINO
Hush, I tell thee, hold thy peace, Wilt the
Stil-le, sag' ich, schwei-ge still! Wirst du
Pap.
Queen? she too is in this place?
was? sie soll im Tem-pel sein?
T.
les-son ne'er be learn-ing Of the priests' mys-te-rious warn-ing?
im-mer so ver-mes-sen dei-ner Ei-des-pflicht ver-ges-sen?
1st & 2nd LADIES
Dost thou not know what must be-fall thee? Hast thou for-
3rd LADY Ta-mi-no hör,' du bist ver-lo-ren! Ge-den-ke
Dost thou not know what must be-fall thee? Hast thou for-
Ta-mi-no hör', du bist ver-lo-ren! Ge-den-ke
1. L.
2. L.
-got the Queen's com-mand? Hast thou not heard what folk are say-ing
an die Kö-ni-gin! Man zi-schelt viel sich in die Oh-ren
3. L.
got the Queen's com-mand? Hast thou not heard what folk are say-ing
an die Kö-ni-gin! Man zi-schelt viel sich in die Oh-ren
fp
tr

1. L.
2. L.
A-bout this tem-ple's wick-ed band?
von die-ser Prie-ster fal-schem Sinn.
3. L.
A-bout this tem-ple's wick-ed band?
von die-ser Prie-ster fal-schem Sinn.
TAMINO
A wise man walks in rea-son's way, Nor cares what
Ein Wei-ser prüft und ach-tet nicht, was der ge-
1. L.
Hast thou not heard what folk are say - ing
Man zi-schelt viel sich in die Oh - ren
2. L.
3. L.
Hast thou not heard what folk are
Man zi-schelt viel sich in die
T.
fool-ish folk may say.
-mei-ne Pö-bel spricht.
A wise man
Ein Wei - - ser
1. L.
A-bout this temple's wicked band?
von die-ser Priester falschem Sinn.
Who joins their band, we know full
Man sagt wer ih-rem Bun-de
2. L.
3. L.
say - ing
Oh - ren
A-bout this temple's wicked band?
von die-ser Priester falschem Sinn.
T.
walks in rea - - son's way.
prüft und ach - - tet nicht,
fp

1.L.
well, Is damn'd to ev-er-last-ing Hell, is damn'd to ev - - er-last - - ing
schwört, der fährt zur Höll' mit Haut und Haar, der fährt zur Höll' mit Haut und
2.L.
Who joins their band, we know full well, Is damn'd to ev-er-last-ing Hell, is damn'd to
Man sagt, wer ih-rem Bunde schwört, der fährt zur Höll' mit Haut und Haar, mit Haut und
3.L.
Who joins their band, we know full well, Is damn'd to ev-er-last-ing
Man sagt, wer ih-rem Bunde schwört, der fährt zur Höll' mit Haut und
fp
fp
1.L.
Hell.
Haar.
2.L.
Hell.
Haar.
3.L.
Hell.
Haar.
PAPAGENO
Oh this is real-ly too in-fer-nal! Must we go to fire e-ter-nal Down be-low?
Das wär' beim Teu-fel, wär' beim Teu-fel, wär' beim Teu-fel, wär' beim Teu-fel un-er-hört!
f
p
TAMINO
'Tis just what fool-ish wo-men say, And those that
Ge-schwätz von Wei-bern nach-ge-sagt, von Heuch-lern
Pap.
Tell me, Ta-mi-no, is that so?
Sag an, Ta-mi-no, ist das wahr?

T.
fear the light of day.
a-ber aus-ge-dacht.
Is not the Queen a wo-man
Sie ist ein Weib, hat Wei-ber-
Pap.
But 'tis the Queen who says 'tis true.
Doch sagt es auch die Kö-ni-gin.
T.
too? Have done, and trust to none but me;
-sinn. Sei still, mein Wort sei dir ge-nug;
Think on thine oath, and
denk' dei-ner Pflicht und
cresc.
f
sf
p
1st & 2nd LADY
So stern, so proud, so staunch to du-ty? And
Wa-rum bist du mit uns so sprö-de? Auch
3rd LADY
So stern, so proud, so staunch to du-ty? And
Wa-rum bist du mit uns so sprö-de? Auch
T.
si-lent be.
hand-le klug.
p
con Ped.
1.L.
2.L.
Pa-pa-ge-no deaf to beau-ty?
Pa-pa-ge-no schweigt, so re-de!
3.L.
Pa-pa-ge-no deaf to beau-ty?
Pa-pa-ge-no schweigt, so re-de!
PAPAGENO
If I could on-ly— say—
Ich möchte ger-ne— woll—

TAMINO
Hush! Hush!
Still! Still!
Pap.
You see my tongue is tied— In truth my chat-ter has no
Ihr seht, dass ich nicht soll— Dass ich nicht kann das Plaudern
1. L.
2. L.
sotto voce
We
Wir
3. L.
sotto voce
We
Wir
T.
In truth thy chat-ter has no end-ing, Thy tongue is wagging night and day
Dass du nicht kannst das Plaudern las-sen ist wahr-lich ei-ne Schand' für dich.
Pap.
end - ing, My tongue is wag - ging night and day.
las - sen, ist wahr-lich ei - ne Schand' für mich.
1. L.
2. L.
must with shame be home-ward wending, Since not one word to us they'll
müs - sen sie mit Scham ver-las-sen, es plau-dert Kei - ner si-cher -
3. L.
must with shame be home-ward wending, Since not one word to us they'll
müs - sen sie mit Scham ver-las-sen, es plau-dert Kei - ner si-cher -
fp

1. L.
say. We must with shame be....... home - ward wend - ing,
-lich. Wir müs-sen sie.... mit..... Scham ver - - las - sen,
2. L.
say. We must with shame be home-ward wending,
-lich. Wir müs-sen sie mit Scham ver - las-sen,
3. L.
say. We must with shame be home-ward wending,
-lich. Wir müs-sen sie mit Scham ver - las-sen,
T.
sotto voce
They must with shame be home-ward wending, Since not one
Sie müs-sen uns mit Scham ver - las-sen, es plau-dert
Pap.
sotto voce
They must with shame be home-ward wending, Since not one
Sie müs-sen uns mit Scham ver - las-sen, es plau-dert
p
1. L.
Since not one word.... to us they'll say. A
es plau-dert Kei - ner si - cher - lich. Von
f
2. L.
Since not one word to us they'll say. A
es plau-dert Kei - ner si - cher - lich. Von
f
3. L.
Since not one word to us they'll say. A
es plau-dert Kei - ner si - cher - lich. Von
f
T.
word to them we'll say. A
Kei - ner si - cher-lich. Von
f
Pap.
word to them we'll say. A
Kei - ner si - cher-lich. Von
f
f

1. L.
2. L.
man's re - solve we can - not shake Who al - ways thinks be -
fe - stem Gei - ste ist ein Mann, er den - ket was er
3. L.
man's re - solve we can - not shake Who al - ways thinks be -
fe - stem Gei - ste ist ein Mann, er den - ket was er
T.
man's re - solve they can - not shake Who al - ways thinks be -
fe - stem Gei - ste ist ein Mann, er den - ket was er
Pap.
man's re - solve they can - not shake Who al - ways thinks be -
fe - stem Gei - ste ist ein Mann, er den - ket was er
p
1. L.
2. L.
- fore he'll speak. A man's re - solve we can - not
spre - chen kann. Von fe - stem Gei - ste ist ein
3. L.
- fore he'll speak. A man's re - solve we can - not
spre - chen kann. Von fe - stem Gei - ste ist ein
T.
- fore he'll speak. A man's re - solve they can - not
spre - chen kann. Von fe - stem Gei - ste ist ein
Pap.
- fore he'll speak. A man's re - solve they can - not
spre - chen kann. Von fe - stem Gei - ste ist ein
f
1. L.
2. L.
shake Who al - ways thinks be - fore he'll speak, who al - ways
Mann, er den - ket, was er spre - chen kann, er den - ket
3. L.
shake Who al - ways thinks be - fore he'll speak,
Mann, er den - ket, was er spre - chen kann,
T.
shake Who al - ways thinks be - fore he'll speak,
Mann, er den - ket, was er spre - chen kann,
Pap.
shake Who al - ways thinks be - fore he'll speak,
Mann, er den - ket, was er spre - chen kann,
p

1. L.
2. L.
thinks be-fore he'll speak,
was er spre-chen kann,
who al-ways thinks before he'll
er den-ket was er spre-chen
3. L.
who al - ways thinks be-fore he'll speak,
er den-ket, was er spre-chen kann,
T.
who al - ways thinks be-fore he'll speak,
er den-ket, was er spre-chen kann,
Pap.
who al - ways thinks be-fore he'll speak,
er den-ket, was er spre-chen kann,
1. L.
2. L.
speak.
kann.
3. L.
who al - ways thinks be-fore he'll speak.
er den - ket was er spre-chen kann.
T.
who al - ways thinks be-fore he'll speak.
er den - ket was er spre-chen kann.
Pap.
who al - ways thinks be-fore he'll speak.
er den - ket was er spre-chen kann.
Tenor
f
What wo - men are those who re -
CHORUS (behind)
Ent - weiht ist die hei - li - ge
Bass
f
cresc
fp
fp

(*Re-enter the Two Priests.*)

1st Priest: Prince, thou hast shown thyself a true man. Come, yet another journey lies before thee. (*He throws a veil over Tamino's head and leads him out.*)

2nd Priest (*to Papageno*)*:* Up, friend, take heart and come with me.

Papageno: What? More journeys? I think Papagena will be an old woman before I come to the end of them. (*The Priest veils him and leads him away.*)

1. *Priester:* Heil dir, Jüngling! Dein standhaft männliches Betragen hat gesiegt. So! Nun komm'!

2. *Priester:* Freund, stehe auf! Sammle dich und sei ein Mann!

Papageno: Bei so einer ewigen Wanderschaft möcht' einem wohl die Liebe auf immer vergehen!

Scene 3. A Garden.

(Pamina discovered lying asleep. Monostatos steals in.)

Monostatos: Ha! There's the disdainful beauty. And it was on her account that I was beaten! *(He comes closer.)* How white she looks! Ah, I've a flaming furnace inside me. Is it safe? Ah, just one little kiss would be something at least.

Monostatos: Ha, da find' ich ja die spröde Schöne! Wenn ich wüsste, dass ich so ganz allein und unbelauscht wäre, ich wagte es noch einmal. Ein Küsschen, dächte ich, liesse sich entschuldigen.

Nº 13 Aria

Allegro

Everything is to be sung and played very softly, as if the music was a very long way off.*)

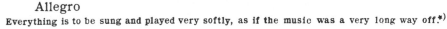

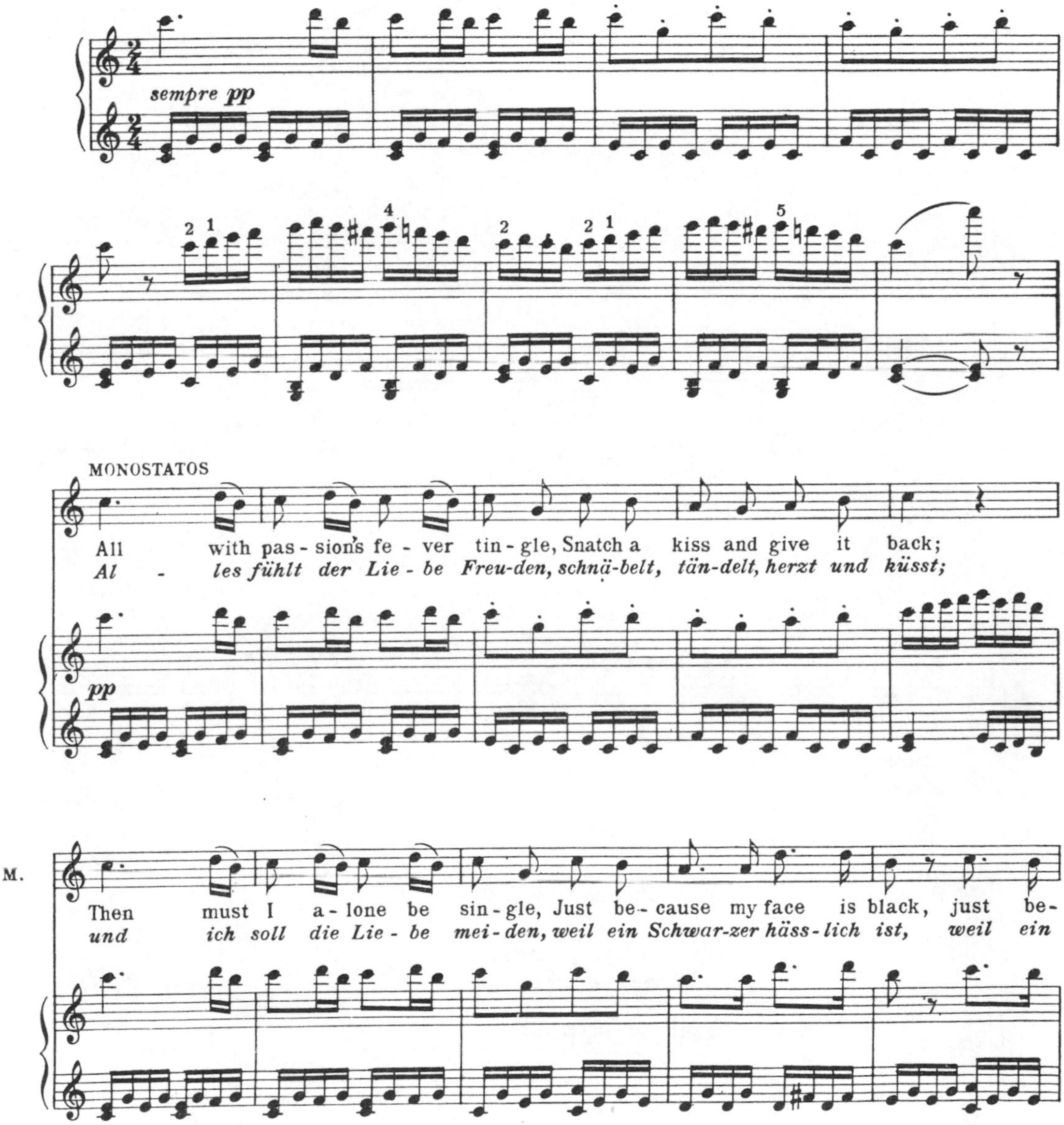

*) *Mozart's own direction.*

M.
cause my face is black?
Schwar-zer häss-lich ist.
Love in-
Ist mir
-deed! can I not feel it? I am man e-nough, I'm
denn kein Herz ge - ge - ben? Ich bin auch den Mäd-chen
sure, I am man e-nough, I'm sure! If I
gut, ich bin auch den Mäd-chen gut! Im - mer
al-ways must con-ceal it, That is more than I'll en-dure, that is more than I'll en-
oh - ne Weib-chen le-ben, wä-re wahr-lich Höl-len-glut, wä-re wahr-lich Höl-len-
-dure, that is more than I'll en-dure.
-glut, wä-re wahr-lich Höl-len-glut.
mfp

M.
Then my plea-sures I'll be
Drum so will ich, weil ich
pp
M.
tak-ing, No temp-ta-tion I'll re-sist; Laws were on-ly made for
le-be, schnä-beln, küs-sen, zärt-lich sein. Lie-ber gu-ter Mond ver-
M.
break-ing, Some one real-ly must be kiss'd, some one real-ly must be kiss'd!
-ge-be, ei-ne Weis-se nahm mich ein, ei-ne Weis-se nahm mich ein.
M.
Now's the time,
Weiss ist schön,
M.
there's no one look-ing— Moon, you dare to play the spy?
ich muss sie küs-sen; Mond, ver-stek-ke dich da-zu,
mfp

M.
Moon, you dare to play the spy? If you think it's all too shock-ing, You should
Mond, ver-stek-ke dich da - zu. Sollt' es dich zu sehr ver-dries-sen, o so
mfp
M.
shut your sil - ly eye, you should shut your sil - ly eye, you should shut your sil - ly eye.
mach' die Au - gen zu, o so mach' die Au - gen zu, o so mach' die Au - gen zu.
He comes close up to PAMINA.

(*The Queen of Night enters from behind.*)

Queen: Avaunt! (*Monostatos starts back.*)

Pamina: Mother!

Monostatos (aside): Mother? That must be the Queen of Night. (*He hides.*)

Queen: Child, where is the young Prince whom I sent to find thee?

Pamina: He has joined the initiates of the temple.

Queen: Then thou art lost to me for ever.

Pamina: No, no, Mother, let us fly this place together, at once.

Queen: 'Tis useless. My power came to an end when thy father died, after handing over to Sarastro the sevenfold Shield of the Sun. There is but one chance. Take this dagger; thou shalt kill Sarastro, and bring the Shield of the Sun to me.

Pamina: But, Mother——

Queen: Not a word!

Königin: Zurück!

Pamina: Mutter! Meine Mutter!

Monostatos: Mutter? Hm, das muss man belauschen.

Königin: Verdank' es der Gewalt, mit der man dich mir entriss, dass ich noch deine Mutter mich nenne! Siehst du hier diesen Stahl? Er ist für Sarastro geschliffen. Du wirst ihn töten und den mächtigen siebenfachen Sonnenkreis auf Sarastro's Brust, den dein Vater vor seinem Tode freiwillig den Eingeweihten übergab, mir überliefern.

Pamina: Aber, liebste Mutter——

Königin: Kein Wort!

Nº 14. Aria

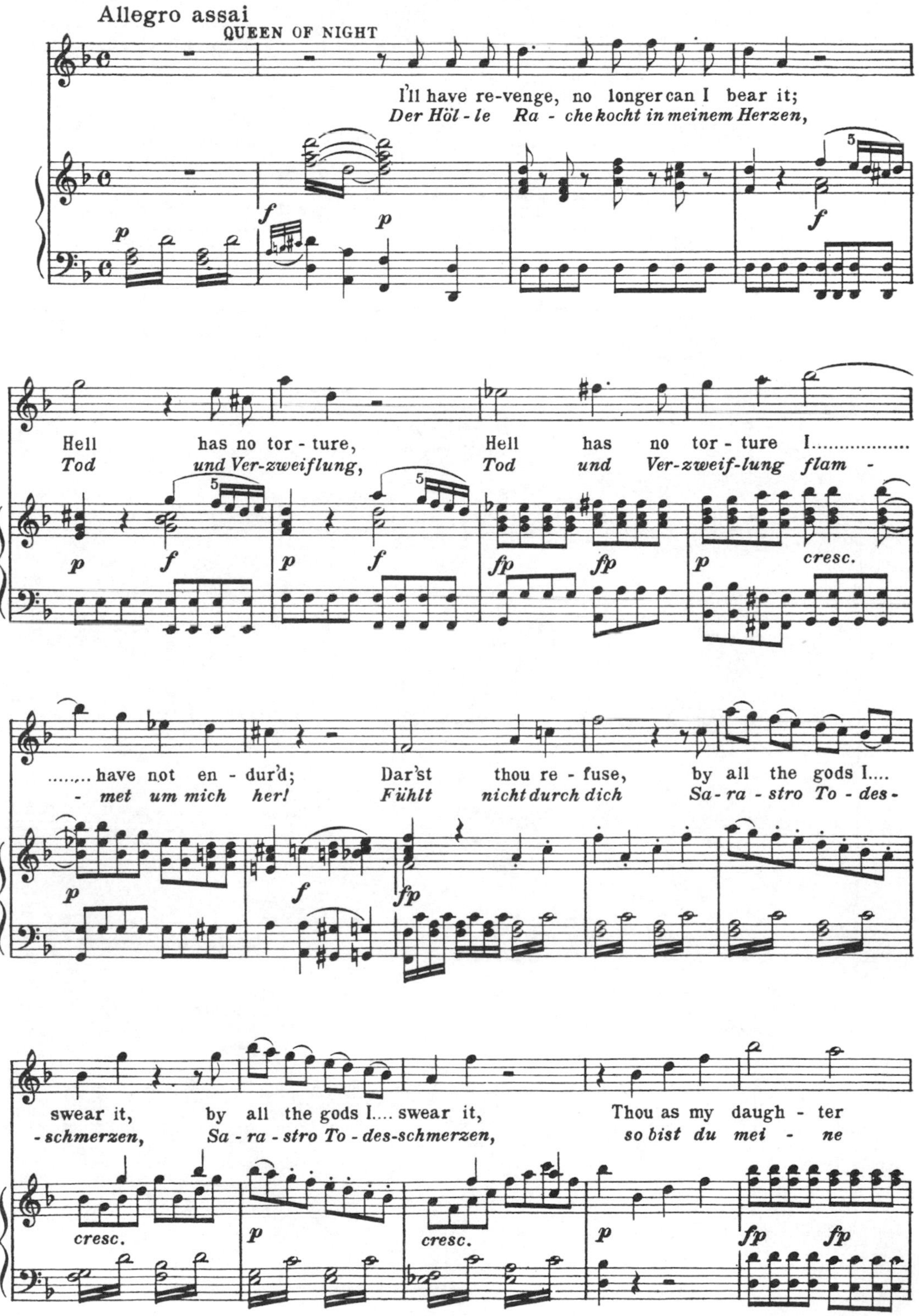
Allegro assai
QUEEN OF NIGHT
I'll have re-venge, no longer can I bear it;
Der Höl - le Ra - che kocht in meinem Herzen,
Qu.
Hell has no tor - ture, Hell has no tor - ture I..................
Tod und Ver-zweiflung, Tod und Ver-zweif-lung flam -
p f p f fp fp p cresc.
Qu.
.... have not en - dur'd; Dar'st thou re - fuse, by all the gods I....
- met um mich her! Fühlt nicht durch dich Sa - ra - stro To - des -
p f fp
Qu.
swear it, by all the gods I.... swear it, Thou as my daugh - ter
- schmerzen, Sa - ra - stro To - des-schmerzen, so bist du mei - ne
cresc. p cresc. p fp fp

Qu.
art for e'er ab-jur'd, for e'er ab - jur'd, as my daughter art ab-
Toch - ter nim-mer-mehr, so bist du mein; mei-ne Toch-ter nim-mer-
sf p
-jur'd, ah
-mehr,
as my daugh - ter
mei - ne Toch - ter
fp
art ab-jur'd, ah
nim - mer-mehr,
f p
thou
so

Qu.
as my daugh - ter art for e'er ab - jur'd.
bist du mei - ne Toch - ter nim - - mer-mehr.
fp
fp
cresc.
f
Qu.
No
Ver-
fp
f
Qu.
time for ten - der yearn-ing, Such fool - ish thoughts be spurn-ing! The
-stos - sen sei auf e - wig, ver-las - sen sei auf e - wig, zer-
p
f
Qu.
fires with-in me burn-ing Con - sume each vi - tal
-trüm - mert sei'n auf e - wig al-le Ban - de der Na -
p.
f
fp
Qu.
part. To ha-tred, to ven-geance they are turning What was
-tur, ver-stos-sen, ver-las - sen und zer-trümmert al-le
p
f

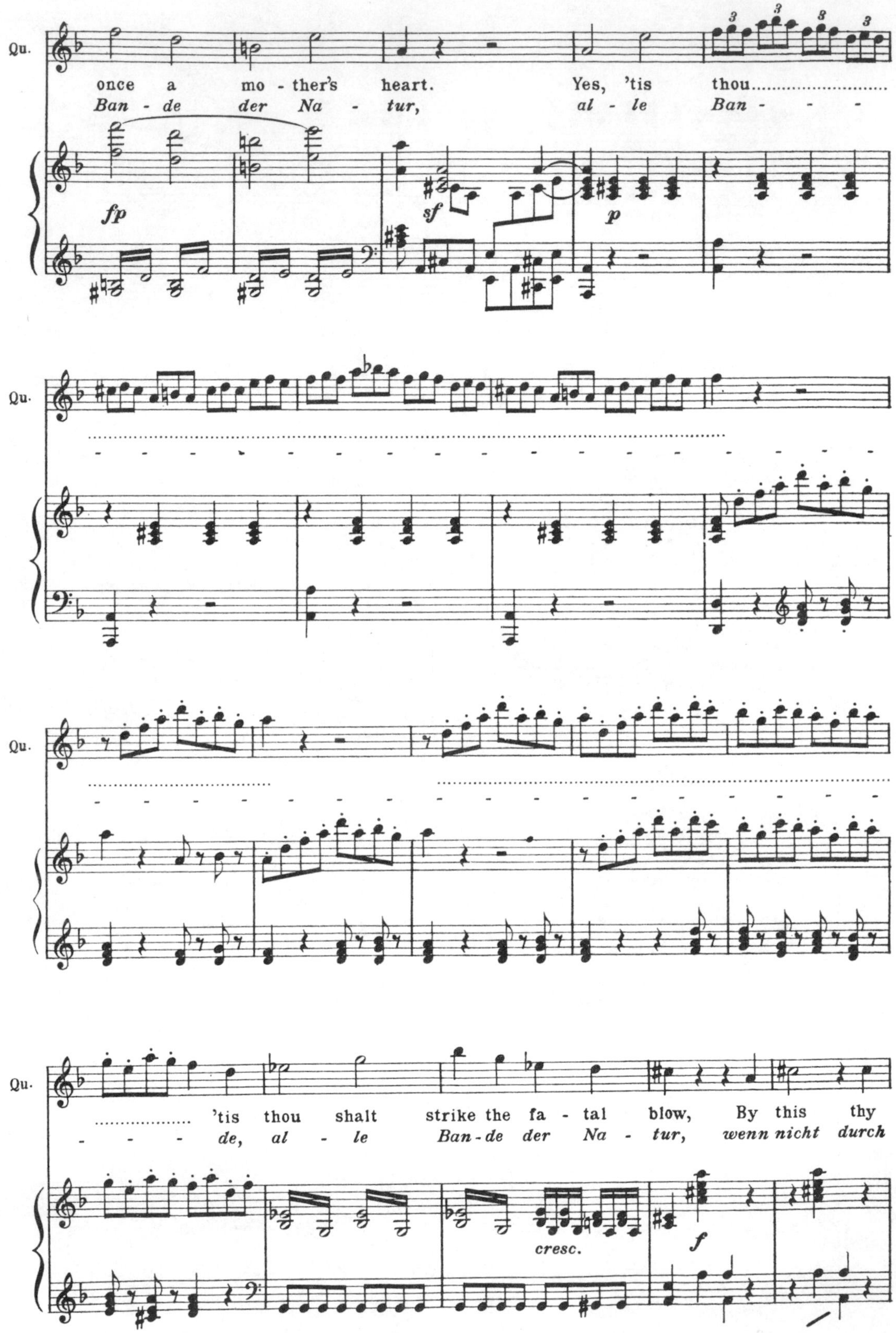
Qu.
once a mo - ther's heart. Yes, 'tis thou
Ban - de der Na - tur, al - le Ban - - -
fp
sf
p
Qu.
Qu.
Qu.
'tis thou shalt strike the fa - tal blow, By this thy
- - - de, al - le Ban - de der Na - tur, wenn nicht durch
cresc.
f

Qu.
nand Sa - ra-stro's might shall crum - ble! Now,
dich Sa - ra-stro wird er - blas - sen! Hört,
f
Qu.
now, now,............ ty-rant, tremble!
hört, hört,............ Ra - che - göt - ter,
sf
She disappears.
Qu.
Gods, re-cord my vow!
hört der Mut - ter Schwur!

Pamina: Kill Sarastro? I cannot, I cannot—— (*Monostatos has crept up behind her, and seizes her suddenly by the wrists.*) Ah!

Monostatos: I have heard all. There is but one way to save thyself and thy mother from Sarastro's wrath.

Pamina: What is it?

Monostatos: Be mine!

Pamina: Never!

Monostatos: No? Then die! (*Sarastro has entered from above, and comes up behind them just in time to hurl Monostatos to the ground.*) Sir, I am innocent. She would have taken thy life, if I had not been just in time to prevent it.

Sarastro: Thy soul is as black as thy face. Go!

Monostatos (*aside, going*)*:* If I can't have the girl, I'll try my luck with the mother.

Pamina: Sir, spare my mother. Her grief at losing me has driven her distracted.

Sarastro: I know all. Thou wilt see how I revenge myself upon her.

Pamina: Morden soll ich? Götter, das kann ich nicht, das kann ich nicht! (*Monostatos kommt schnell.*) Ha!

Monostatos: Du hast nur einen Weg, dich und deine Mutter zu retten.

Pamina: Der wäre?

Monostatos: Mich zu lieben. Ja oder Nein?

Pamina: Nein!

Monostatos: Nein? So fahre denn hin! (*Sarastro, der rasch hinzugetreten, schleudert Monostatos zurück.*) Herr, ich bin unschuldig!

Sarastro: Ich weiss, dass deine Seele ebenso schwarz als dein Gesicht ist. Geh!

Monostatos: Jetzt such' ich die Mutter auf, weil die Tochter mir nicht beschieden ist.

Pamina: Herr, strafe meine Mutter nicht! Der Schmerz über meine Abwesenheit——

Sarastro: Ich weiss alles. Allein, du sollst sehen, wie ich mich an deiner Mutter räche.

Nº 15. Aria

Larghetto
SARASTRO
We know no thought of.... ven - geance With-
Here each to ev - 'ry.... o - ther By
In die - sen heil' - gen Hal - len kennt
In die - sen heil' - gen Mau - ern wo
p
f
p
S.
- in these tem - ple... walls, Where love leads back to.....
mu - tual love is..... bound; Where ev - 'ry wrong finds
man die Ra - che... nicht, und ist ein Mensch ge -
Mensch den Men - schen liebt, kann kein Ver - rä - ter
S.
du - ty Who - e'er from du - ty... falls; By friendship's
par - don, No trai - tor e'er is... found. Those whom this
-fal - len, führt Lie - be ihn zur Pflicht. Dann wan - delt
lau - ern, weil man dem Feind ver - gibt. Wen sol - che
S.
kind - ly.... hand........held fast, He finds the land of.... light......... at
bond can not......... u - nite Are all un - worth - y..... of............ the
er.... an Freun - des Hand ver - gnügt und froh in's bess' - re
Leh - ren nicht..... er - freu'n, ver - die - net nicht ein Mensch zu

S.
last, by friendship's kind - ly hand held fast,.... he finds the
light, those whom this bond can not u - nite,.... are all un -
Land, dann wan-delt er an Freun - des Hand... ver-gnügt und
sein, wen sol - che Leh - ren nicht er - freu'n, ver - die - net
S.
land of....... light at last,.... by friendship's kind - ly hand held
- worth - y........ of the light,... those whom this bond can not u -
froh in's.... bess' - re Land,.. dann wan-delt er an Freun - des
nicht ein....Mensch zu sein,.... wen sol - che Leh - ren nicht er -
S.
fast, he finds the land of light at last, the land........ of
- nite, are all un - worth - y of the light, un - worth - y, un -
Hand ver-gnügt und froh in's bess'- re Land, in's bess' - re, in's
- freu'n, ver - die - net nicht ein Mensch zu sein, ein Mensch, ein
S.
light.... at...... last.
- worth - y of the light.
bess' - - re....... Land.
Mensch zu...... sein.
D.S.
D.S.
Fine

Scene 4. A Hall.

(*Tamino and Papageno are led in by two Priests.*)

1st Priest: You are to remain here alone. When the trumpets sound, proceed that way. Prince, farewell. Once more, remember: Silence!

2nd Priest: Papageno, he that breaks silence in this place, is struck down by lightning. Farewell. (*Exeunt Priests.*)

Papageno: Tamino!

Tamino: Sh!

Papageno: This is a merry life! I wish I were out in the woods again, to hear the birds sing.

Tamino: Sh!

Papageno: I suppose I may talk to myself!

Tamino: Sh!

Papageno (*sings*)*:* La, la, la! Not so much as a drop of water to be had here, let alone anything else. (*An ugly old woman enters with a cup of water.*) Is that for me?

Old Woman: Yes, love.

Papageno (*looks at her a long time, and drinks*)*:* Water, nothing more or less. Tell me, fair damsel, are all strangers here treated as nobly as this?

Old Woman: To be sure they are, love.

Papageno: Then there will be very few that come here.

Old Woman: Yes, very few.

Papageno: I thought as much. Sit down here, grandmother, and talk to me. How old are you?

Old Woman: Just eighteen.

Papageno: Just eighty?

Old Woman: Just eighteen.

Papageno: Ha! ha! Have you got a sweetheart?

Old Woman: To be sure I have.

Papageno: And is he as young as you are?

Old Woman: Not quite—he's a little older.

Papageno (*laughs*)*:* And what's his name?

Old Woman: Papageno.

Papageno (*frightened*)*:* Papageno? (*Pause.*) Where is this Papageno of yours?

Old Woman: Why, there. (*Points straight at Papageno.*)

Papageno: I your sweetheart?

Old Woman: To be sure, love!

Papageno: Then who are you?

Old Woman: My name is—— (*Thunder—she hobbles away quickly.*)

Papageno: Oh! oh! (*Tamino looks at him.*) I'll never speak another word.

1. *Priester:* Hier seid ihr euch beide allein überlassen. Sobald die Posaune tönt, dann nehmt ihr euren Weg dahin! Prinz, leb' wohl! Noch einmal vergesst das Wort nicht: Schweigen!

2. *Priester:* Papageno! Wer an diesem Orte sein Stillschweigen bricht, den strafen die Götter durch Donner und Blitz. Leb' wohl!

Papageno: Tamino!

Tamino: St!

Papageno: Das ist ein lustiges Leben! Wär' ich lieber in meiner Strohhütte, oder im Walde, so hört' ich doch manchmal einen Vogel pfeifen!

Tamino: St!

Papageno: Mit mir selbst werd' ich wohl sprechen dürfen.

Tamino: St !

Papageno: La la la! Nicht einmal einen Tropfen Wasser bekommt man bei diesen Leuten, viel weniger sonst was. (*Ein altes hässliches Weib kommt mit einem Becher mit Wasser.*) Ist das für mich?

Altes Weib: Ja, mein Engel!

Papageno: Nicht mehr und nicht weniger als Wasser. Sag' du mir, du unbekannte Schöne, werden alle fremden Gäste auf diese Art bewirtet?

Altes Weib: Freilich, mein Engel!

Papageno: So, so! Auf diese Art werden die Fremden auch nicht gar zu häufig kommen.

Altes Weib: Sehr wenig.

Papageno: Kann mir's denken. Geh', Alte, setz' dich her zu mir. Sag' du mir, wie alt bist du denn?

Altes Weib: Achtzehn Jahr' und zwei Minuten.

Papageno: Achtzig Jahr' und zwei Minuten.

Altes Weib: *Achtzehn* Jahr' und zwei Minuten.

Papageno: Ha, ha, ha! Ei, du junger Engel! Hast du auch einen Geliebten?

Altes Weib: I freilich!

Papageno: Ist er auch so jung wie du?

Altes Weib: Nicht ganz; er ist um zehn Jahre älter.

Papageno: Wie nennt sich denn dein Liebhaber?

Altes Weib: Papageno.

Papageno: Papageno?—Wo ist er denn, dieser Papageno?

Altes Weib: Da sitzt er, mein Engel!

Papageno: Ich wär' dein Geliebter?

AltesWeib: Ja, mein Engel!

Papageno: Sag' du mir, wie heisst du denn?

Altes Weib: Ich heisse——

Papageno: O weh! Nun sprech' ich kein Wort mehr!

Nº 16. Terzetto

Enter the THREE GENII carrying a table spread with food and drink, the flute and the bells.

Allegretto
p
1st & 2nd GENII
Be-fore the gates we once did meet you,
And set your feet in wisdom's way;
Seid uns zum zwei-ten-mal willkom-men,
ihr Männer in Sa-ra-stros Reich!
3rd GENIUS
Be-fore the gates we once did meet you,
And set your feet in wis-dom's way;
Seid uns zum zwei-ten-mal willkom-men,
ihr Männer in... Sa-ra-stros Reich!
1. G.
2. G.
Now for the se-cond time we greet you
With-in the tem-ple walls to-day.
Er schickt, was man euch ab-ge-nom-men,
die Flö-te und die Glöckchen euch.
3. G.
Now for the se-cond time we greet you
With-in the tem-ple walls to-day.
Er schickt, was man euch ab-ge-nom-men,
die Flö-te und die Glöckchen euch.

1. G.
2. G.
Take now the flute and bells to cheer you, Good cheer for wea-ry limbs receive;
Wollt ihr die Spei-sen nicht verschmähen, so es-set, trin-ket froh da-von!
3. G.
Take now the flute and bells to cheer you, Good cheer for wea-ry limbs receive;
Wollt ihr die Spei-sen nicht verschmähen, so es-set, trin-ket froh da-von!
1. G.
2. G.
When for the third time we draw near you, Vir-tue shall per-fect joy achieve.
Wenn wir zum drit-ten-mal uns se-hen, ist Freu-de eu-res Mu-tes Lohn.
3. G.
When for the third time we draw near you, Vir-tue shall per-fect joy achieve.
Wenn wir zum drit-ten-mal uns se-hen, ist Freu-de eu-res Mu-tes Lohn.
1. G.
2. G.
Prince, be thou brave, light thou shalt see;
Ta-mi-no, Mut! Nah' ist das Ziel.
3. G.
Prince, be thou brave, light thou shalt see;
Ta-mi-no, Mut! Nah' ist das Ziel.

Papageno: Tamino! Here's something to eat at last. (*Tamino walks about, playing the flute.*) Well, blow away! I mean to blow my belly out. (*Drinking.*) This is wine for the gods!

Papageno: Tamino, wollen wir nicht speisen? Blase du nur fort auf deiner Flöte; ich will meine Brocken blasen! Ha! das ist Götterwein!

(*Enter Pamina.*)

Pamina: At last I find thee! I heard the flute and followed the sound. But thou art silent! (*Tamino turns away.*) Hast thou not a word for Pamina? (*He motions her to go away. She turns to Papageno.*) Papageno, tell me, what ails him? (*Papageno, his mouth full, motions her away.*) You, too? Tamino! Tamino! thou lovest me no longer.

Pamina: Gütige Götter! Dank euch! Ich hörte deine Flöte—und so lief ich pfeilschnell dem Tone nach. Aber du bist traurig? Sprichst nicht eine Silbe mit deiner Pamina? Liebst du mich nicht mehr? O das ist mehr als Kränkung, mehr als Tod!

Nº 17 Aria

Andante
PAMINA
Ah, 'tis gone, 'tis gone for e - ver, Hap-py..... dream, 'twill ne'er come true, hap-py
Ach, ich fühl's, es ist ver-schwunden, e - wig... hin der Lie - be... Glück, e - wig
p
Pam.
dream, 'twill ne'er come true; Ne'er a - gain re-turn to cheer me Hours of
hin der Lie - be Glück! Nim-mer kommt ihr, Won - ne - stun - den, mei - nem
f
p
Pam.
joy that once....... I knew, ne'er... re - turn.... those hours of... joy
Her-zen mehr..... zu-rück, mei - nem Her - zen, mei - nem Her - - - - -
Pam.
.... that once...... I knew. O Ta-mi-no, on - ly
- - zen mehr........ zu-rück! Sieh', Ta-mi-no, die - se
mfp
mfp
Pam.
hear me! Must I suf - fer thy dis-dain, thy......... dis-dain? If no long-er thou dost
Trä-nen fliessen, Trau-ter, dir al - lein, dir........... al - lein! Fühlst du nicht der Lie - be

Pam.
love me, no long-er lov'st me, On - ly death can end my pain, can end my
Sehnen, der Lie-be Seh-nen, so wird Ru - he, so wird Ruh' im...To - de
Pam.
pain. If no long-er thou dost love me, if no long-er thou dost love me, On - ly...
sein; fühlst du nicht der Lie-be Seh-nen, fühlst du nicht der Lie - be Seh-nen, so.........wird
cresc.
f
p
Pam.
death, yes, on - ly...death can end my pain, on - ly death.... can end....... my pain, can end my
Ru - he, so.....wird Ruh' im To - de sein, so wird Ruh'...... im To - - de sein, im To-de
Exit.
Pam.
pain, can end...........my..pain.
sein, im To - - de...sein.
p
cresc.
f
p

Papageno: You see I can keep silence as well as anyone. (*Drinks. The trumpets are heard. Tamino signs to him to go.*) Go on then. I'll come directly; haven't I followed you everywhere? (*Trumpets. Tamino pulls his arm.*) But tell me, Tamino, what is to be the end of all this? (*Tamino points to heaven.*) Ask the gods, must I? (*Tamino nods.*) Well, they can at least tell us more than *we* know. (*Trumpets. Tamino drags him across the stage.*) Not so fast, not so fast; we're in time enough to be plucked and roasted! (*Tamino pulls him out.*)

Papageno: Nicht wahr, Tamino, ich kann auch schweigen, wenn's sein muss? (*Der Bläserakkord ertönt.*) Geh' du nur voraus; ich komme schon nach! Heiss' du mich einen Schelmen, wenn ich dir nicht in allem folge! (*Der Bläserakkord ertönt abermals.*) Aber hör' einmal, Tamino, was wird denn noch alles mit uns werden? (*Tamino deutet gen Himmel.*) Die Götter soll ich fragen? Ja, die könnten uns freilich mehr sagen, als wir wissen! (*Der Bläserakkord tönt noch einmal.*) Eile nur nicht so! Wir kommen noch immer zeitig genug, um uns braten zu lassen.

Scene 5. A Vault.

No. 18 Chorus

Pr.
place he will be ta - king. From false - hood's
Dien - ste ganz er - ge - ben. Sein Geist ist
place he will be ta - king. From false - hood's
Dien - ste ganz er - ge - ben. Sein Geist ist
place he will be ta - king. From false - hood's
Dien - ste ganz er - ge - ben. Sein Geist..... ist
taint his mind is free, from false-hood's taint
kühn, sein Herz ist rein, sein Geist ist kühn,
taint his mind is free, from false-hood's taint
kühn, sein Herz ist rein, sein Geist ist kühn,
taint his mind...... is free, from false - hood's taint his
kühn, sein Herz........ ist rein, sein Geist ist kühn, sein
his mind is free, Soon, soon, full - ness of light he
sein Herz ist rein, bald, bald, bald wird er un - ser
his mind is free, Soon, soon, full - ness of light he
sein Herz ist rein, bald, bald, bald wird er un - ser
mind is free, Soon, soon, full - ness of light he
Herz ist rein, bald, bald, bald wird er un - ser

(*Tamino is led in*)

Sarastro: Prince, thou hast borne thyself so far with manly composure. There remain yet before thee two paths of danger. If thy heart still beats for Pamina, if thou still hast the desire to reign as a wise king in the appointed time, then may the gods guard thee safe upon thy way! Thy hand! Let Pamina be brought in. (*Exeunt two Priests, and re-enter with Pamina, veiled.*)

Pamina: Where am I? (*Pause.*) How dreadful is this silence! Tell me, where is Tamino?

Sarastro: He waits to take his last farewell of thee.

Pamina: His last farewell? (*The Priests remove her veil.*) Tamino! (*She moves towards him; he motions her back.*)

Sarastro: Prinz, dein Betragen war bisher männlich und gelassen; nun hast du noch zwei gefährliche Wege zu wandern. Schlägt dein Herz noch ebenso warm für Pamina und wünschest du einst als ein weiser Fürst zu regieren, so mögen die Götter dich ferner begleiten! Deine Hand! Man bringe Pamina!

Pamina: Wo bin ich? Welch' eine fürchterliche Stille!—Saget, wo ist mein Jüngling?

Sarastro: Er wartet deiner, um dir das letzte Lebewohl zu sagen.

Pamina: Das letzte Lebewohl?—Tamino!

Tamino: Zurück!

Nº 19 Terzetto

Andante moderato

Pam.
dan - ger's yet im - pending, Thy doom some aw - ful death may be.
To - de nicht ent-ge-hen, mir flüstert die - ses Ahn - dung ein.
T.
What-e'er the
Der Göt - ter
S.
What-e'er the
Der Göt - ter
Pam.
Oh lov-edst
O lieb-test
T.
gods to me be send-ing, Their will my law shall al - ways be.
Wil - le mag ge - sche-hen, ihr Wink soll mir Ge - set - ze sein!
S.
gods to him be send-ing, Their will his law shall al - ways be.
Wi - le mag ge - sche - hen, ihr Wink soll ihm Ge - set - ze sein!
Pam.
thou with my de - vo - tion, So calm a mien thou could'st not show, so calm a
du, wie ich dich lie - be, du würdest nicht so ru - hig sein, du würdest
l.h.
r.h.
r.h.

Pam.
mien thou could'st not show.
nicht so ru - hig sein.
T.
I feel no less that sweet e - mo-tion, And am thine
Glaub' mir, ich füh - le glei-che... Trie - be, werd' e-wig
S.
He feels no less that sweet e - mo-tion, And is thine
Glaub' mir, er füh - let glei - che Trie - be, wird e-wig
T.
own where-'er I go, and am thine own.......where'er I.... go.
dein Ge-treu - er sein, werd' e-wig dein...... Ge - treu-er... sein.
S
own where-'er he go, and is thine own.......where'er he... go. The hour is
dein Ge-treu - er sein, wird e-wig dein...... Ge - treu-er... sein. Die Stunde
Pam.
We part, and part per-chance for e - ver.
Wie bit - ter sind der Tren-nung Lei - den!
T.
We part, and part per-chance for e - ver.
Wie bit - ter sind der Tren-nung Lei - den!
S.
come that bids you se - ver. The hour is
schlägt, nun müsst ihr schei-den. Die Stun-de

Pam.
T.
S.
We part, and part perchance for e - ver.
Wie bit - ter sind der Trennung Leiden!
We part, and part perchance for e - ver.
Wie bit - ter sind der Trennung Leiden!
The hour is
Pa - mi - na
come that bids you se - ver.
schlägt, nun müsst ihr schei - den!
The hour is come, he must a -
Ta - mi - no muss nun wie - der
O cru - el hour, canst thou not stay?
Ta - mi - no muss nun wirk - lich fort.
Ta -
Ta -
come I must a - way, must a - way.
ich muss wirk - lich fort, wirk - lich fort!
We part, and part per - chance for
Wie bit - ter sind der Tren - nung
- way, must a - way.
fort, wie - der fort!
The hour is come that bids you se - ver,
Die Stunde schlägt, nun müsst ihr schei - den!
the hour is
Ta - mi - no
- mi - no!
- mi - no!
Ta - mi - no!
Ta - mi - no!
thou must a -
So musst du
e - ver. The hour is come, I... must a - way,
Lei - den! Pa - mi - na ich muss wirklich fort,
I must a - way!
nun muss ich fort!
come, he must a - way, he must a - way,
muss nun wie - der fort, nun wie - der fort,
he must a - way!
nun muss er fort!
l.h.

Pam.
T.
S.
- way! thou must a - way! Ta -
fort! so musst du fort! Ta -
I must a-way! Pa - mi-na,
nun muss ich fort! Pa - mi-na,
he must a - way!
nun muss er fort!
- mi - no, fare thee well! fare thee well! fare thee well,........ ah,...........
- mi - no, le - be wohl! le - be wohl! le - be, le - be,............
fare thee well! fare thee well! fare thee well,........ ah,...........
le - be wohl! le - be wohl! le - be, le - be,............
Thou must a-way, the call o - bey, Ta-mi-no, Ta-mi-no,
Nun ei - le fort, dich ruft dein Wort! nun ei-le, nun ei-le,
fare thee well! Blest hours of rapture,
le - be.... wohl! Ach gold'- ne Ru-he,
ıare thee well! Blest hours of rapture,
le - be.... wohl! Ach gold'- ne Ru-he,
the hour is come, the call o - bey! The hour is come, the call o -
nun ei - le fort, dich ruft dein Wort. Die Stunde schlägt, die Stunde
mf

Pam.
T.
S.
Blest hours of rapture, ah! re - turn ye, ah! re -
ach, gold'-ne Ru-he, keh - re wie-der! keh-re,
Blest hours of rapture, ah! re - turn ye, ah! re -
ach, gold'-ne Ru-he, keh - re wie-der! keh-re,
- bey, The hour is come, The call o-bey that bids you se-ver,
schlägt, die Stunde schlägt, die Stunde schlägt, wir sehn uns wie-der,
- turn ye.... ne - - ver? Fare thee
keh - - re wie - - der! Le - be
- turn ye.... ne - - ver? Fare thee...
keh - - re wie - - der! Le - be......
Yet not for e - ver,
wir sehn uns wie - der!
Exeunt omnes.
well, fare thee well!
wohl! Le - be... wohl!
well, fare thee well!
wohl! Le - be wohl!
yet not for e - ver!
wir sehn uns wie - der!

Scene 6. A Hall.

Papageno (behind): Tamino! Tamino! (*Enters.*) Have you left me for ever? If I only knew where I was! Tamino! Tamino! Don't desert me this time, and I'll never disobey you again. (*Going.*)

A Voice: Stand back!

Papageno (starting back): Oh, oh! which way? which way? If I could only find the door where I came in! (*Makes for the opposite side.*)

Another Voice: Stand back!

Papageno: No way out, forwards or backwards. I shall have to die of starvation here. It serves me right; why did I ever go with him?

(*Enter a Priest.*)

Priest: Wretched man, thy punishment should be to wander for ever in the dark passages of the earth. But the gods are merciful, and pardon thee; yet wilt thou never know the joys of the initiated.

Papageno: Well, there are plenty of men like me. The greatest joy I can think of would be a good cup of wine.

Priest: Hast thou no further desires?

Papageno: Not at present.

Priest: Thou shalt have thy wish. (*Exit. A cup is handed in.*)

Papageno: Ha, there's the wine! (*Drinks.*) That's good. Now I'm happy. (*Drinks.*) I feel so strange. There's something I want still —something—what is it, I wonder?

Papageno: Tamino! Tamino! Willst du mich denn gänzlich verlassen? Wenn ich nur wenigstens wüsste, wo ich wäre!—Tamino! Tamino! Nur diesmal verlass' mich armen Reisegefährten nicht!

Eine Stimme: Zurück!

Papageno: Barmherzige Götter! Wo wend' ich mich hin? Wenn ich nur wüsste, wo ich hereinkam!

Eine andere Stimme: Zurück!

Papageno: Nun kann ich weder vorwärts, noch zurück! Muss vielleicht am Ende gar verhungern! Schon recht! Warum bin ich mitgereist?

Priester: Mensch! Du hättest verdient, auf immer in finsteren Klüften der Erde zu wandern. Die gütigen Götter aber entlassen dich der Strafe. Dafür aber wirst du das himmlische Vergnügen der Eingeweihten nie fühlen.

Papageno: Je nun, es gibt noch mehr Leute meines Gleichen. Mir wäre jetzt ein gut' Glas Wein das grösste Vergnügen.

Priester: Hast du sonst keinen Wunsch in dieser Welt?

Papageno: Bis jetzt nicht.

Priester: Man wird dich damit bedienen!

Papageno: Juchhe! da ist er schon! Herrlich! Himmlisch! Göttlich! Ha! ich bin jetzt so vergnügt, dass ich bis zur Sonne fliegen wollte! Mir wird ganz wunderlich um's Herz! Ich möchte—ich wünschte—ja, was denn?

No. 20 Aria

Pap.
round; I should not feel so lone - ly,.... Had I a sweet-heart
sich, o, so ein sanf-tes Täub - chen wär' Se - lig - keit.... für....
8
found, had I a sweetheart found, had I.... a.... sweetheart found.
mich, wär' Se - lig- keit..für.... mich, wär' Se - lig - keit..für.... mich!
Bells
Allegro
Then life would be no-thing but
Dann schmeckte mir Trin-ken und
p
plea - sure; I'd en - vy no mon-arch his trea - sure. No need to learn wis-dom in
Es - sen, dann könnt' ich mit Für-sten mich mes - sen, des Le-bens als Wei-ser mich
cresc.
there;.. 'Twere wis-dom e-nough and to spare, I'd en - vy no mon-arch his
freu'n... und wie im E - ly - si-um sein, dann könnt' ich mit Für-sten mich
fp

Pap.
trea-sure. No need to learn wis-dom in there;....'Twere wis-dom e-nough and to spare,
mes-sen, des Le-bens als Wei-ser mich freu'n..... und wie im E-ly-si-um sein,
cresc.
fp
Pap.
e-nough and to spare, e-nough and to spare.
im E-ly-si-um sein, im E-ly-si-um sein!
Andante
Bells
p
PAPAGENO
'Tis love, they say, love on-ly, That makes the world go.....
Ein Mäd-chen o-der Weib-chen wünscht Pa-pa-ge-no.....
p
Pap.
round; I should not feel so lone-ly,... Had I a sweet-heart
sich, o, so ein sanf-tes Täub-chen wär' Se-lig-keit....für....

Pap.
found, had I a sweet-heart found, had I... a.... sweet-heart found.
mich, wär' Se - lig-keit... für... mich, wär' Se- lig- keit... für.... mich!
Bells
Allegro
Pap.
But no, there's not one that will
Ach, kann ich denn Kei-ner von
Pap.
take me, Con-ten-ted and hap-py to make me; If none will give ear to my sigh,... In-
al - len den rei-zen-den Mädchen ge - fal - len? Helf' ei - ne mir nur aus der Not,..... sonst
cresc.
fp
Pap.
-deed of des-pair I shall die, But no, there's not one that will
gräm' ich mich wahr-lich zu Tod; ach, kann ich denn Kei-ner ge -
Pap.
take me, If none will give ear to my sigh,....... In-deed of des-pair I shall die,
-fal - len? Helf' ei - ne mir nur aus der Not,......sonst gräm' ich mich wahr lich zu Tod,
cresc.
fp

Pap.
of des-pair I shall die, of des-pair I shall die.
mich wahrlich zu Tod, mich wahrlich zu Tod.
Andante
Bells
p
PAPAGENO
'Tis
Ein
Pap.
love, they say, love on - ly, That makes the world go.. round; I should not feel so
Mäd-chen o - der Weib - chen wünscht Pa - pa - ge - no... sich, o, so ein sanf-tes
Pap.
lone - ly,... Had I a sweet-heart found, had I a sweet-heart found, had
Täub - chen wär' Se - lig - keit.. für... mich, wär' Se - lig - keit.. für... mich, wär'

Allegro
Pap.
I... a... sweetheart found.
Se-lig-keit für mich!
Each day sees me weaker and frai - ler, Each day I grow thinner and pa - ler; Was
Wird Kei-ne mir Lie-be ge-wäh - ren, so muss mich die Flamme ver-zeh - ren; doch
e'er such a sickness as this?.. For me there's no cure but a kiss, Was e'er such a
küsst mich ein weib-li-cher Mund, so bin ich schon wieder ge-sund; doch küsst mich ein
cresc.
fp
sick-ness as this?... Was e'er such a sick-ness as this?..... For me there's no cure but a
weib-li - - cher Mund, doch küsst mich ein weib-li-cher Mund,... so bin ich schon wieder ge -
cresc.
fp
kiss, no cure but a kiss, no cure but a
-sund, schon wie-der ge - sund, schon wie-der ge -

(The Old Woman enters, dancing and singing.)

Old Woman: Here I am, love.

Papageno: So *you* have taken pity on me?

Old Woman: Yes, love; and if you'll swear to be true to me all the days of your life, you shall see how tenderly your little wife will love you.

Papageno: Oh, you sweet little darling!

Old Woman: Come, give me your hand and promise.

Papageno: Not so fast, love; I'll think it over.

Old Woman (seriously): Papageno, I warn thee, delay not. Thy hand, at once, or thou art imprisoned here for ever.

Papageno: Imprisoned?

Old Woman: Yes; to live on bread and water, and never to see any one again for the rest of thy days.

Papageno: For the rest of my days? Well, better an old wife than none at all! There! (*Gives her his hand.*) I'll be true to thee (*aside*) until I see someone prettier.

Old Woman: Swear it!

Papageno: I swear it! (*She is transformed into a young woman, covered with feathers.*) Pa-pa-papagena! (*Enter Priest.*)

Priest: Away! He is not yet worthy of thee. (*He drags her out. Papageno attempts to follow; the Priest pushes him back.*) Stand back! (*Exit Priest with Papagena.*)

Papageno (running after them): Papagena! Papagena! (*Off.*)

Altes Weib.: Da bin ich schon, mein Engel!

Papageno: *Du* hast dich meiner erbarmt?

Altes Weib: Ja, mein Engel! Und wenn du mir versprichst, mir ewig treu zu bleiben, dann sollst du sehen, wie zärtlich dein Weibchen dich lieben wird.

Papageno: Ei, du zärtliches Närrchen!

Altes Weib: Komm', reiche mir zum Pfand unseres Bundes deine Hand!

Papageno: Nur nicht so hastig, lieber Engel. So ein Bündnis braucht doch auch seine Überlegung.

Altes Weib: Papageno, ich rate dir, zaud're nicht. Deine Hand, oder du bist auf immer hier eingekerkert.

Papageno: Eingekerkert?

Altes Weib: Wasser und Brot wird deine tägliche Kost sein. Ohne Freund, ohne Freundin musst du leben und der Welt auf immer entsagen.

Papageno: Wasser trinken? Der Welt entsagen? Nein, da will ich doch lieber eine Alte nehmen, als gar keine. Nun, da hast du meine Hand mit der Versicherung, dass ich dir immer getreu bleibe, (*für sich*) so lang' ich keine Schönere sehe.

Altes Weib: Das schwörst du?

Papageno: Ja, das schwör' ich! (*Das alte Weib verwandelt sich in ein junges Mädchen, welches ebenso gekleidet ist, wie Papageno.*) Pa-pa-papagena!

Priester: Fort! Er ist deiner noch nicht würdig! (*Papageno will nach.*) Zurück! sag' ich.

Papageno: Papagena! Papagena!

Scene 7. A Garden. The THREE GENII are discovered.

Nº 21. Finale

1. G.
- store the reign of light and love, Make mortal men like gods a - bove, make mortal men like gods a -
ist die Erd' ein Himmel - reich, und Sterb-liche sind Göttern gleich, und Sterb-liche sind Göttern
2. G.
- store the reign of light and love, Make mortal men like gods a - bove, make mortal men like gods a -
ist die Erd' ein Himmel - reich, und Sterb-liche sind Göttern gleich, und Sterb-liche sind Göttern
3. G.
- store the reign of light and love, Make mortal men like gods a - bove, make mortal men like gods a -
ist die Erd' ein Himmel - reich, und Sterb-liche sind Göttern gleich, und Sterb-liche sind Göttern
fp
PAMINA has entered with wild gestures, carrying a dagger.
1. G.
- bove. But look, what maid is that des-pairing? Our help she's needing.
gleich. Doch seht, Verzweif lung quält Paminen! Sie ist von Sinnen!
2. G.
- bove. Pa-mi-na 'tis! For slighted
gleich. Wo ist sie denn? Sie quält ver-
3. G.
- bove. Pa-mi-na 'tis! For slighted
gleich. Wo ist sie denn? Sie quält ver-
p
1. G.
For slight-ed love her heart is bleed - ing, Let us to her be comfort
Sie quält verschmähter Lie-be Lei - den. Lasst uns der Armen Trost be -
2. G.
love her heart is bleed - ing, Let us to her be com - fort
-schmäh - ter Lie - be Lei - den. Lasst uns der Ar - men Trost be -
3. G.
love her heart is bleed - ing, Let us to her be com - fort
-schmäh - ter Lie - be Lei - den. Lasst uns der Ar - men - Trost be -
mf
p

1. G.
2. G.
3. G.
bear-ing. Un-hap-py child, 'twere sad in truth To........ lose ....
-rei - ten! Fürwahr ihr Schick - sal geht uns nah'! O......... wä - - -
bear-ing. Un-hap-py child, 'twere sad in truth..... To lose the
-rei - ten! Fürwahr ihr Schicksal geht uns nah'!...... O wä-re
bear-ing. Un-hap-py child, 'twere sad in truth...... To lose the
-rei - ten! Fürwahr ihr Schicksal geht uns nah'!...... O wä-re
mf
p
....the love of that fair youth. She comes; let us remain un-seen, To watch what
- re nur ihr Jüng-ling da! Sie kommt; lasst uns bei Sei-te gehn, da-mit wir,
love of that fair youth. She comes; let us remain un-seen, To watch what
nur ihr Jüng-ling da! Sie kommt; lasst uns bei Sei-te gehn, da-mit wir,
love of that fair youth. She comes; let us remain un-seen, To watch what
nur ihr Jüng-ling da! Sie kommt; lasst uns bei Sei-te gehn, da-mit wir,
PAMINA
No other
Du al-so
this wild air may mean, re-main to watch what this wild air may mean.
was sie ma-che, sehn, da-mit, da-mit wir, was sie ma-che, sehn!
They draw aside.
this wild air may mean, to watch what this wild air may mean.
was sie ma-che, sehn, da - mit wir, was sie ma-che, sehn!
this wild air may mean, let us re-main to watch what this wild air may mean.
was sie ma-che, sehn, damit wir, was sie ma-che, was sie ma-che, sehn!

Pam.
way but this re-mains, To make an end.... of all my pains.
bist mein Bräuti-gam? Durch dich voll - end'... ich meinen Gram!
1st & 2nd GENII
What dreadful
Welch' dunkle
1. G.
words are these we hear? Her grief to mad - ness brings her
Wor - te sprach sie da? Die Ar-me ist dem Wahn - sinn
2. G.
words are these we hear? Her grief to madness brings her
Wor - te sprach sie da? Die Ar-me ist dem Wahnsinn
3. G.
What dreadful words are these we hear? Her grief to mad - ness brings her
Welch' dunkle Wor - te sprach sie da? Die Ar-me ist dem Wahn - sinn
PAMINA
O Death, be - lo-vèd, I am thine; Re-fuse not thou, re-fuse not thou this heart of
Geduld, mein Trau-ter, ich bin dein; bald werden wir, bald werden wir vermäh-let
1. G.
near.
nah'.
2. G.
near.
nah'.
3. G.
near.
nah'.
mfp

Pam.
mine, refuse not thou this heart of mine.
sein, bald werden wir ver-mäh - let sein!
1st & 2nd GENII
Ah! 'tis madness in her wak-ing;
Wahn - sinn tobt ihr im Ge - hir - ne,
3rd GENIUS
Ah! 'tis madness in her wak-ing;
Wahn - sinn tobt ihr im Ge - hir - ne,
mf
p
mfp
fp
They advance towards her.
1. G.
2. G.
Haste, ere she her life be tak - ing! Dear Pa - mi - na,... turn this...
Selbst-mord steht auf ih-rer Stir - ne. Hol - des Mäd - chen, sieh' uns
3. G.
Haste, ere she her life be tak - ing! Dear Pa - mi - na, turn this...
Selbst-mord steht auf ih-rer Stir - ne. Hol - des Mäd - chen, sieh' uns
fp
PAMINA
Death is wel - come, since the day...When Ta-mi-no could for-
Ster- ben will ich, weil der Mann, den ich nimmermehr kann
1. G.
2. G.
way.
an!
3. G.
way.
an!
cresc.

She shows the dagger.
Pam.
-sake me; Yet to hate him nought can make me. This to me my mo-ther gave.
has-sen, sei-ne Trau-te kann ver-las-sen. Dies gab mei-ne Mut-ter mir.
fp
Pam.
Bet-ter thus to end my an-guich, Than in hope -
Lie-ber durch dies Eisen ster-ben, als durch Lie -
1st & 2nd GENII
Know'st thou what's beyond the grave?
Selbst-mord stra-fet Gott an dir!
3rd GENIUS
Know'st thou what's beyond the grave?
Selbst-mord stra-fet Gott an dir!
fp
f
Pam.
-less love to languish; Mother! Mother! by thy gift I'll die; From thy curse I cannot
-bes-gram ver-der-ben! Mutter, Mutter, durch dich lei-de ich und dein Fluch ver-folget
fp
fp
Pam.
fly.
mich!
Ah! my sor-rows who can
Ha! des Jammers Mass ist
1st & 2nd GENII
Mai-den, come away with us.
Mädchen, willst du mit uns gehn?
3rd GENIUS
Mai-den, come away with us.
Mädchen, willst du mit uns gehn?
p

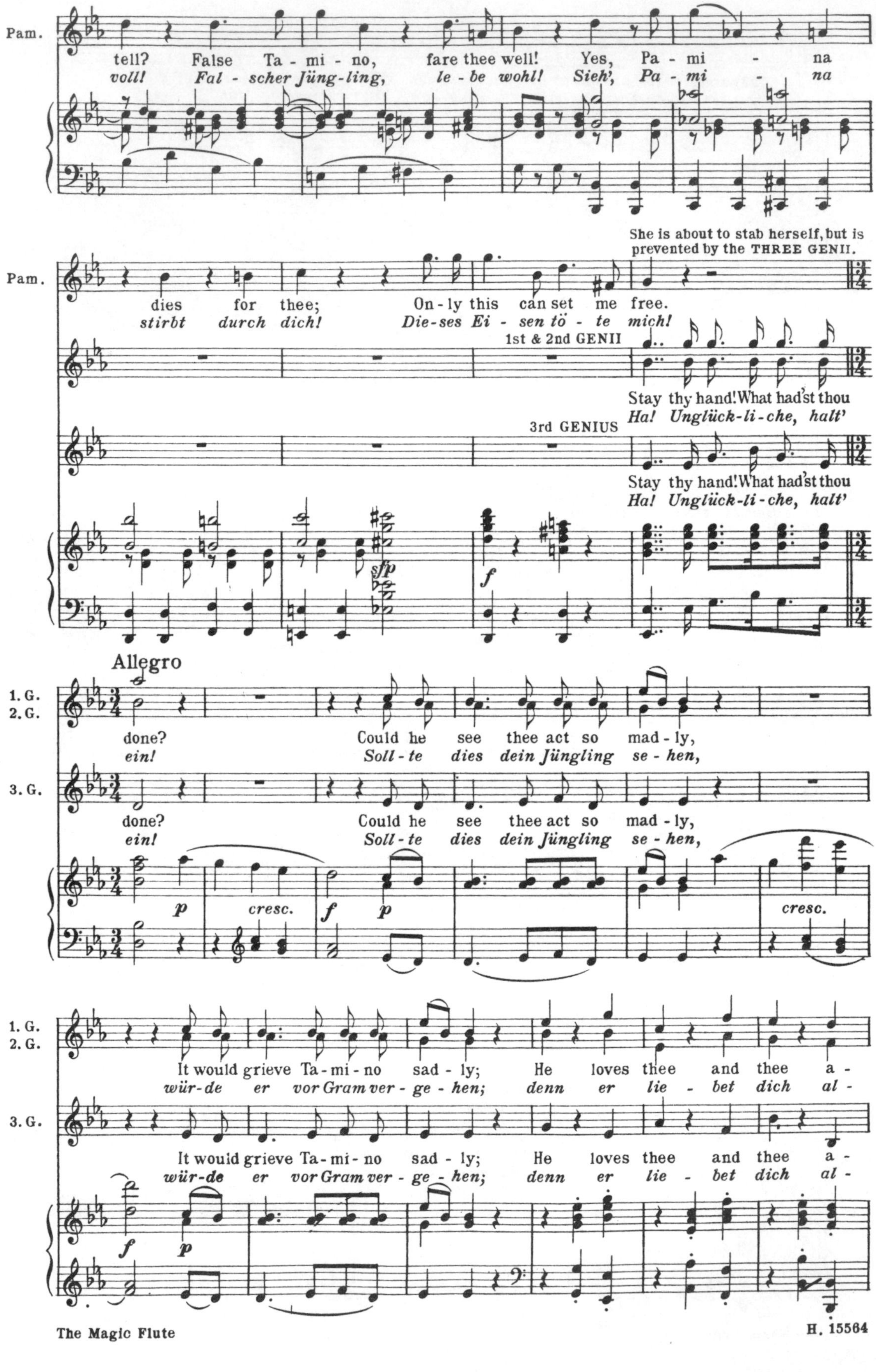
Pam.
tell? False Ta - mi - no, fare thee well! Yes, Pa - mi - na
voll! Fal - scher Jüng - ling, le - be wohl! Sieh', Pa - mi - na
She is about to stab herself, but is prevented by the THREE GENII.
Pam.
dies for thee; On - ly this can set me free.
stirbt durch dich! Die - ses Ei - sen tö - te mich!
1st & 2nd GENII
Stay thy hand! What had'st thou
Ha! Unglück - li - che, halt'
3rd GENIUS
Stay thy hand! What had'st thou
Ha! Unglück - li - che, halt'
sfp
f
Allegro
1. G.
2. G.
done? Could he see thee act so mad - ly,
ein! Soll - te dies dein Jüngling se - hen,
3. G.
done? Could he see thee act so mad - ly,
ein! Soll - te dies dein Jüngling se - hen,
p
cresc.
f
p
cresc.
1. G.
2. G.
It would grieve Ta - mi - no sad - ly; He loves thee and thee a -
wür - de er vor Gram ver - ge - hen; denn er lie - bet dich al -
3. G.
It would grieve Ta - mi - no sad - ly; He loves thee and thee a -
wür - de er vor Gram ver - ge - hen; denn er lie - bet dich al -
f
p

PAMINA
What? in faith-ful love a - bi-ding, His de-sire he could be hiding? Turn'd his face from me a -
Was? er füh - let Ge-gen-lie - be, und ver-barg mir sei-ne Triebe, wandte sein Gesicht von
1. G.
2. G.
- lone.
- lein.
3. G.
- lone.
- lein.
Pam.
- way, To Pa - mi - na nought would say?
mir? Wa-rum sprach er nicht mit mir?
1st & 2nd GENII
Ask no
Die-ses
3rd GENIUS
Ask no
Die-ses
p
cresc.
f
p
1. G.
2. G.
more, the reason's hid-den. Now to fetch thee we are bid-den; Soon Ta -
müs - sen wir ver-schweigen, doch wir wol - len dir ihn zei-gen, und du
3. G.
more, the reason's hid-den. Now to fetch thee we are bid-den; Soon Ta -
müs - sen wir ver-schweigen, doch wir wol - len dir ihn zei-gen, und du
cresc.
f
p

1. G.
2. G.
- mi - no thou shalt see, How he still is true to thee, Yes, for thee would
wirst mit Staunen sehn, dass er dir sein Herz ge-weiht und den Tod für
3. G.
- mi - no thou shalt see, How he still is true to thee, Yes, for thee would
wirst mit Staunen sehn, dass er dir sein Herz ge-weiht und den Tod für
cresc.
PAMINA
Lead me on, no long-er stay.
Führt mich hin, ich möcht' ihn sehn!
1. G.
2. G.
e - ven die! Then to him let us a - way.
dich nicht scheut. Komm, wir wol - len zu ihm gehn.
3. G.
e - ven die! Then to him let us a - way.
dich nicht scheut. Komm, wir wol - len zu ihm gehn.
f p cresc. f p f p
Pam.
Lead me on, no lon-ger stay,.... no lon-ger
Führt mich hin, ich möcht ihn sehn, ich möcht ihn
1. G.
2. G.
Then to him let us a - way, then to
Komm, wir wol - len zu ihm gehn, komm, wir
3. G.
Then to him let us a - way, then to
Komm, wir wol - len zu ihm gehn, komm, wir
cresc. f p

Pam.
stay,..... O lead me on,........ no lon-ger stay!................. When love has
sehn,.... ich möcht' ihn sehn,.... ich möcht' ich sehn!................. Zwei Her - zen,
1.G.
2.G.
him let us a - way................... When love has
wol - - len zu ihm gehn!................. Zwei Her - zen,
3.G.
him let us a - way. .... When love has
wol - - len zu ihm gehn!................. Zwei Her - zen,
cresc.
p
Pam.
join'd two hearts...for e-ver, No pow'r of man those
die von Lie - be bren-nen, kann Men - schen-ohn - macht
1.G.
2.G.
join'd two hearts...for e-ver, No pow'r of man those
die von Lie - be bren-nen, kann Men - schen-ohn - macht
3.G.
join'd two hearts for e-ver, No pow'r of man those
die von Lie - be bren-nen, kann Men - schen-ohn - macht
mfp
Pam.
hearts can se-ver. Fear they no danger or a-larm; The
nie - mals tren-nen. Ver - lo - ren ist der Feinde Müh', die
1.G.
2.G.
hearts can se-ver. Fear they no danger or a-
nie - mals tren-nen. Ver - lo - ren ist der Feinde
3.G.
hearts can se-ver. Fear they no
nie - mals tren-nen. Ver - lo - - - ren
mfp

Pam.
gods will guard them safe from harm. The gods will guard,
Göt - ter selb - sten schützen sie, die Göt - ter, Göt - - - - - - -
1.G.
2.G.
-larm; The gods will guard them safe from harm, the gods will guard them
Müh', die Göt - ter selb - sten schützen sie, die Göt - ter selb - sten
3.G.
dan - - - ger or a - - larm; The gods will guard them
ist.............. der Fein - - - - de Müh', die Göt - ter selb - sten
mfp
mfp
Pam.
.... will guard.... them safe...... from harm, will guard them safe from
- - - ter selb - sten schüt - zen sie, die Göt - - ter.... schüt - zen
p
1.G.
2.G.
safe.... from harm. The gods.... will guard.... them safe.....from
schüt - zen sie, die Göt - ter selb - sten schüt - zen
p
3.G.
safe from harm. The gods will guard them safe from
schüt - zen sie, die Göt - ter selb - sten schüt - zen
p
fp
Pam.
harm, will guard them safe from harm, safe.... from
sie, die Göt - - ter.... schüt - zen sie, schüt - zen
f
1.G.
2.G.
harm, the gods..... will guard.... them safe...... from harm, safe..... from
sie,..... die Göt - - ter selb - - sten schüt - zen sie, schüt - zen
f
3.G.
harm, the gods will guard them safe from harm, safe from
sie, die Göt - - ter selb - - sten schüt - zen sie, schüt - zen
f
f
p

THE GENII lead PAMINA away.

Scene 8

TWO MEN in armour are seen standing at each side of a doorway. TAMINO is brought in by Priests.

Tenor
TWO MEN in armour.
Who treads the path of toil that un-to
Der, wel-cher wan-delt die-se Stras-se
Bass
Who treads the path of toil that un-to
Der, wel-cher wan-delt die-se Stras-se
2 M.
wis-dom lead-eth, His soul the
voll Be-schwer-den, wird rein durch
wis-dom lead-eth, His soul the
voll Be-schwer-den, wird rein durch
2 M.
purge of fire and wa-ter need-eth.
Feu-er, Was-ser, Luft und Er-den.
purge of fire and wa-ter need-eth.
Feu-er, Was-ser, Luft und Er-den.
2 M.
When him the aw-ful fear of death nomore can
Wenn er des To-des Schrecken ü-ber-win-den
When him the aw-ful fear of death nomore can
Wenn er des To-des Schrecken ü-ber-win-den

2 M.
fright, Then may he rise to gain the
kann, schwingt er sich aus der Er - de
fright, Then may he rise to gain the
kann, schwingt er sich aus der Er - de
2 M.
sa - cred height. There with th'en - -
him - mel - an. Er - leuch - tet
sa - cred height. There with th'en - -
him - mel - an. Er - leuch - tet
2 M.
- light - en'd shall he take his place, To
wird er dann im Stan - de sein, sich
- light - en'd shall he take his place, To
wird er dann im Stan - de sein, sich
2 M.
know the mys - tic rite of I - sis face to face.
den My - ste - ri - en der I - sis ganz zu weih'n.
know the mys - tic rite of I - sis face to face.
den My - ste - ri - en der I - sis ganz zu weih'n.

TAMINO
The fear of death shall ne-ver shake me; Let me to vir - - - tue's path be-
Mich schrecktkein Tod, als Mann zu han-deln, den Weg der Tu - - - gend fort zu
T.
-take me. The gates of hor - - - ror o - - - pen wide, I'll seek the
wan-deln. Schliesst mir die Schrek - - kens-pfor - - - ten auf! Ich wa-ge
fp
fp
f
PAMINA's voice is heard outside.
Ta-mi-no, stay! Oh wait for
Ta-mi-no, halt! Ich muss dich
T.
truth what-e'er be - tide.
froh den küh - - - nen Lauf.
p
fp
Allegretto
Pam.
me!
sehn!
T.
Pa-mi-na? I heard her call-ing.
Was hör' ich? Pa - mi - nens Stim-me?
TWO MEN in armour.
Yes, yes, that was Pa-mi-na
Ja, ja, das ist Pa-mi-nens
Yes, yes, that was Pa-mi-na
Ja, ja, das ist Pa-mi-nens
Allegretto
p

T.
At last to fol-low me she's free; To part us now no fate.... has.....
Wohl mir! nun kann sie mit mir gehn, nun tren-net uns kein Schick-sal........
2 M.
call-ing. At last to fol-low thee she's free; To part you now no fate.... has......
Stim-me! Wohl dir! nun kann sie mit dir gehn, nun tren-net euch kein Schick-sal.......
call-ing. At last to fol-low thee she's free; To part you now no fate has
Stim-me! Wohl dir! nun kann sie mit dir gehn, nun tren - - net euch kein Schicksal
T.
power, Though death a - wait us.... in this hour. though death a - wait us... in this
mehr, wenn auch der Tod...be - schie-den wär', wenn auch der Tod... be-schie-den
2 M.
power, Though death a - wait you in this hour. though death a - wait you in this
mehr, wenn auch der Tod beschieden wär', wenn auch der Tod... be-schie-den
power, Though death a - wait you in this hour. though death a - wait you in this
mehr, wenn auch der Tod be - schie-den wär', wenn auch der Tod be-schie-den
T.
hour. To speak with her am I per-mit-ted? Oh
wär! Ist mir er- laubt, mit ihr zu spre-chen? Welch'
2 M.
hour. Yes, now to speak art thou per-mit - ted.
wär! Dir ist er-laubt, mit ihr zu spre-chen.
hour. Yes, now to speak art thou per-mit - ted.
wär! Dir ist er-laubt, mit ihr zu spre-chen.
mf

T.
2 M.
joy.... to find her once a - gain, And hand in hand our end at -
Glück, wenn wir uns wie - der - sehn, froh Hand in Hand in Tem-pel
Re - joice to find her once a - gain, And hand in
Welch' Glück, wenn wir euch wie - der - sehn, froh Hand in
Re - joice to find her once a - gain, And hand in
Welch' Glück, wenn wir euch wie - der - sehn, froh Hand in
p
tain! A maid that fears not death's dark night Is
gehn! Ein Weib, das Nacht und Tod nicht scheut, ist
hand your end at - tain! A maid that fears not death's dark night Is
Hand in Tem - pel gehn! Ein Weib, das Nacht und Tod nicht scheut, ist
hand your end at - tain! A maid that fears not death's dark night Is
Hand in Tem - pel gehn! Ein Weib, das Nacht und Tod nicht scheut, ist
fp fp fp fp fp fp f p
wor-thy to be-hold the light, is wor-thy to be-hold the light.
wür-dig und wird ein - ge-weiht, ist wür-dig und wird ein - ge-weiht.
wor-thy to be-hold the light, is wor-thy to be-hold the light.
wür-dig und wird ein - ge-weiht, ist wür-dig und wird ein - ge-weiht.
wor-thy to be-hold the light, is wor-thy to be-hold the light.
wür-dig und wird ein - ge-weiht, ist wür-dig und wird ein - ge-weiht.
p

PAMINA is brought in.
PAMINA
Andante
O found at...... last! O faith-ful
Ta-mi-no..... mein! O welch' ein
p
Pam.
heart!
Glück!
TAMINO
O hope..... ful--fill'd! No more we part.
Pa-mi-na...... mein! O welch' ein Glück.
T.
Be-hold the gates of hor-ror, Where pain and death a-
Hier sind die Schreckens-pfor-ten, die Not und Tod mir
PAMINA
E'en in that place of... ter-ror I ne'er will leave thy side. Nay,
Ich wer-de al-ler Or-ten an dei-ner Sei-te sein. Ich
T.
-bide.
dräu'n.
cresc.
fp
Pam.
I'll be guide for thee, As love is guide for me: What though the path with thorns be
selb-sten füh-re dich, die Lie-be lei-tet mich. Sie mag den Weg mit Ro-sen

Pam.
strown When love's own ro-ses there have blown? Then take the ma-gic........flute and
streu'n, weil Ro-sen stets bei Dor-nen sein. Spiel' du die Zau-ber - - flö - te
Pam.
play;... Its note gives light on........ dan-ger's...way. That flute from
an; sie schüt - ze uns auf....... uns - rer.... Bahn! Es schnitt in
Pam.
mys - - tic tree was car - ven, And round it might-y spells were wo - ven; The
ei - - ner Zau-ber - stun - de mein Va - ter sie aus tief - stem Grun - de der
Pam.
sa - cred bough my fa-ther tore, Nor fear'd the light - - nings'
tau - send-jähr'-gen Ei-che aus, bei Blitz und Don - - ner,
fp
Ped.
Pam.
thund' - - - rous roar. Then take the... ma - gic flute and play; Its note gives
Sturm und Braus. Nun komm und spiel' die Flö - te an, sie lei - te
fp
p
Ped.

Pam.
light... on........ dan - - ger's way. That sound.... of.... ma - - gic has..................
uns..... auf....... grau - - ser... Bahn! Wir wan - deln durch des To - - -
TAMINO
That sound...... of..... ma - - gic...
Wir wan - deln durch..... des...
TWO MEN in armour
That sound of.... ma - - gic...
Ihr wan-delt durch..... des...
That sound of.... ma - - gic...
Ihr wan-delt durch..... des...
Pam.
.... the pow'r... To... guard us safe..... in.... death's... dread hour. That
- - - nes Macht.. froh durch des To - - des... dü - - st're Nacht. Wir
T.
has....... the pow'r To............ guard us... safe in death's... dread hour. That sound.. of..
To - - nes Macht froh......... durch des... To - - des dü - - st're Nacht. Wir wan - deln
2 M.
has...... the pow'r To guard you safe..... in death's... dread hour.
To - - nes Macht froh durch des To - - des dü - - st're Nacht.
has....... the pow'r To guard you safe in death's dread hour.
To - - nes Macht froh durch des To - - des dü - st're Nacht.

Pam.
sound........ of.... ma - gic... has........ the... pow'r To........... guard us... safe in
wan - deln durch des To - nes Macht froh.......... durch des To - des
T.
ma - - gic has....................... the pow'r.... To... guard us safe....... in
durch des To - - - - - - nes Macht froh durch des To - des
That sound of.... ma - gic has........ the... pow'r To........... guard you... safe........ in
2 M.
Ihr wan-delt durch des To - - nes Macht froh durch des To - - des
That sound of.... ma - gic... has........ the... pow'r To guard you safe........ in
Ihr wan-delt durch des To - - nes Macht froh durch des To - - des
Pam.
death's.... dread hour, death's..dread hour, death's...dread hour.
dü - - st're Nacht, dü - st're Nacht, dü - st're Nacht.
T.
death's.... dread hour, death's..dread hour, death's dread hour.
dü - - st're Nacht, dü - st're Nacht, dü - st're Nacht.
louder
death's.... dread hour, death's dread hour, death's dread hour.
dark
dark
dark
2 M.
dü - - st're Nacht, dü - st're Nacht, dü - st're Nacht.
death's dread hour, death's dread hour, death's dread hour.
dü - st're Nacht, dü - st're Nacht, dü - st're Nacht.
mfp
p
mfp
p
take
T&P USR
exit

MARCH
TAMINO and PAMINA enter the door and are seen to pass through fire. TAMINO plays the flute.
Adagio
p
PAMINA
When fires of pas-sion did as-sail us, Un-
Wir wan - del-ten durch Feu-er-glu - ten, be-
TAMINO
When fires of pas-sion did as-sail us, Un-
Wir wan - del-ten durch Feu-er-glu - ten, be-
Pam.
-scath'd by scorching flame we stood. The voice of mu - sic will not fail us When
-kämpf - ten mu - tig die Ge-fahr. Dein Ton sei Schutz in Was-ser-flu-ten, so....
T.
-scath'd by scorching flame we stood. The voice of mu - sic will not fail us When
-kämpf - ten mu - tig die Ge-fahr. Dein Ton sei Schutz in Was-ser-flu-ten, so....

Pam.
sor - row's wa-ters rise in flood, The voice of mu - sic will not fail us When
wie er es im Feu-er war, dein Ton sei Schutz in Was-ser - flu - ten, so....
T.
sor - row's wa-ters rise in flood, The voice of mu - sic will not fail us When
wie er es im Feu-er war, dein Ton sei Schutz in Was-ser - flu - ten, so....
They pass through water, TAMINO again playing the flute.
Pam.
sor - row's wa-ters rise in flood.
wie er es im Feu - er war!
T.
sor - row's wa-ters rise in flood.
wie er es im Feu - er war!

SARASTRO and the Priests welcome them into the temple.

Ch.
you the rite im-parts; Come! come! come! come!
Wei - - he ist nun dein! Kommt, kommt, kommt, kommt,
you the rite im-parts; Come! come! come!
Wei - - he ist nun dein! Kommt, kommt, kommt,
you the rite im-parts; Come! come! come!
Wei - - he ist nun dein! Kommt, kommt, kommt,
you the rite im-parts; Come! come! come!
Wei - - he ist nun dein! Kommt, kommt, kommt,
Ch.
o - - pen stands the tem-ple door, o - pen stands the door, come! come!
tre - - tet in den Tem-pel ein, in den Tem - - pel ein, kommt kommt,
come! o - - pen, o-pen stands the tem - - ple door, come!
kommt, tre - - tet, tre-tet in den Tem - - pel ein, kommt,
come! o - - pen, o-pen stands the tem - - ple door, come!
kommt, tre - - tet, tre-tet in den Tem - - pel ein, kommt,
come! o - - pen stands the tem-ple door, come!
kommt, tre - - tet in den Tempel ein, kommt,

Ch.
come! o - - pen stands the tem-ple door, come! come!
kommt, tre - - tet in den Tem-pel ein, kommt, kommt,
come! o - - pen stands the tem-ple door, come!
kommt, tre - - tet in den Tem-pel ein, kommt,
come! o - - pen stands the tem-ple door, come!
kommt, tre - - tet in den Tem-pel ein, kommt,
come! o - - pen stands the tem-ple door, come!
kommt, tre - - tet in den Tem-pel ein, kommt,
TAMINO and PAMINA enter the temple.
Ch.
come! o - - pen stands the tem-ple door.
kommt, tre - - tet in den Tempel ein!
come! o - - pen stands the tem-ple door.
kommt, tre - - tet in den Tempel ein!
come! o - - pen stands the tem-ple door.
kommt, tre - - tet in den Tempel ein!
come! o - - pen stands the tem-ple door.
kommt, tre - - tet in den Tempel ein!

Scene 9. A Garden.

Pap.
chat-ter-ing all day and night Lost me the maid, and serve me right, lost me the
plauder-te, und das war schlecht, und drum geschieht es mir schon recht,......drum ge-
mfp
p
Pap.
maid, and serve me right. Yes, e-ver
-schieht es mir schon recht. Seit ich ge-
Pap.
since I drank that wine, E-ver since
-ko - stet die - sen Wein, seit ich das
Pap.
I that maid did see, 'Tis all on fire this heart of mine, And ve-ry soon mad shall I
schö - ne Weib - chen sah, so brennt's im Her-zens-kämmerlein, so zwickt es hier, so zwickt es
Pap.
be. Pa-pa-ge-na! dost thou fly me? Pa-pa-ge - na! don't de-ny me. All in
da. Pa-pa-ge-na, Her-zens-weibchen! Pa-pa-ge - na, lie-bes Täubchen! 's ist um-
cresc.
f
p

Pap.
vain, she will not hear me. Life has no-thing more to cheer me; Bet-ter far it were to
-sonst, es ist ver-ge-bens! Mü-de bin ich mei-nes Le-bens. Ster-ben macht der Lieb' ein
Pap.
die,........ Than en-dure such pain, say I. Here's a
End',......wenn's im Her-zen noch so brennt. Die-sen
Pap.
rope my sighs to stran-gle; At the end of this I'll
Baum da will ich zie-ren, mir an ihm den Hals zu-
Pap.
dan-gle. No more use for me.. has life If.... I can-not find.. a wife. Earth, no
-schnüren, weil das Le-ben mir miss-fällt. Gu-te Nacht, du schwarze Welt! Weil du
Pap.
more shalt thou de-ceive me; Since thou ne'er a mate wilt give me, Then I'll say fare-well to
bö-se an mir handelst, mir kein schö-nes Kind zu-bandelst, so ist's aus, so ster-be

Pap.
thee. All fair maids, oh think of me! all fair maids, oh think of me!
ich. Schö - ne Mäd-chen, denkt an mich, schö - ne Mäd-chen, denkt an mich!
fp
'Tis not yet... too late to save me; If but one fair maid will
Will sich ei - ne um mich Ar - men, eh' ich hän-ge, noch er -
have me, I will die a - no - ther day. Here I am, what do you say? here I
-bar - men, wohl, so lass' ich's dies - mal sein. Ru-fet nur: ja, o - der nein, ru-fet
am, what do you say? Are you si - lent, are you
nur: ja, o - der nein! Kei-ne hört mich; Al - les
si - lent, Not a word re - ply - ing? Must I real - ly then be dy - ing? Pa-pa-
stil - le, Al - les, Al - les stil - le! Al - so ist es eu - er Wil - le? Pa-pa-
fp fp f p

Pap.
-ge - no, take the rope!....... Die thou must, there's no more hope, Pa-pa-ge - no, take the
-ge - no, frisch hin - auf,......... en-de dei - nen Le-bens-lauf! Pa-pa-ge - no, frisch hin-
rope!..... Die thou must, there's no more hope. Well, there's still a chance, I'll
-auf,....... en-de dei - nen Le-bens-lauf! Nun, ich war-te noch, es
wait, there's still a chance, well, I'll wait; I'll...count
sei! ich war - te noch, nun, es sei! bis.. man
three ere 'tis too late. One! Two!
zäh - let: eins, zwei, drei! Eins! Zwei!
(plays)
Andante
Three! Not an an - swer to be heard; Then I must ful - fil my word. No-thing
Drei! Nunwohl-an, es bleibt da-bei, nunwohl-an, es bleibt da-bei; weil mich
p

He prepares to hang himself;
Pap.
can me now re-strain; Fare thee well, thou world of pain, fare thee well, thou world of
nichts zu-rük-ke hält, gu-te Nacht, du fal-sche Welt, gu-te Nacht, du fal-sche
Allegretto
the THREE GENII enter and prevent him.
1.G.
Not yet, not yet, O Pa-pa-ge-no; wait, we pray; Thou hast but
Halt' ein, halt' ein, o Pa-pa-ge-no, und sei klug; man lebt nur
2.G.
Not yet, not yet, O Pa-pa-ge-no; wait, we pray; Thou hast but
Halt' ein, halt' ein, o Pa-pa-ge-no, und sei klug; man lebt nur
3.G.
Not yet, not yet, O Pa-pa-ge-no; wait, we pray; Thou hast but
Halt' ein, halt' ein, o Pa-pa-ge-no, und sei klug; man lebt nur
Pap.
pain.
Welt!
Allegretto
cresc.
f
p
1.G.
one life, throw it not a-way, thou hast but one life, throw it not a-way.
ein-mal, dies sei dir ge-nug, man lebt nur ein-mal, dies sei dir ge-nug!
2.G.
one life, throw it not a-way, thou hast but one life, throw it not a-way.
ein-mal, dies sei dir ge-nug, man lebt nur ein-mal, dies sei dir ge-nug!
3.G.
one life, throw it not a-way, thou hast but one life, throw it not a-way.
ein-mal, dies sei dir ge-nug, man lebt nur ein-mal, dies sei dir ge-nug!
PAPAGENO
Your mer-ry
Ihr habt gut
l.h.

Pap.
jest - ing pray con - tin - ue; But if you felt that fire with -
re - den, habt gut scher- zen; doch brennt' es euch wie mich im
r.h.
l.h.
r.h.
Pap.
- in you You'd fol - low pret - ty maids, like me, you'd fol - low pret - ty maids, like
Her - zen, ihr wür- det auch nach Mäd - chen gehn, ihr wür- det auch nach Mäd - chen
1.G.
2.G.
Then set the ma - gic bells a - ring - ing; 'Tis they thy sweetheart will be bring - ing.
So las - se dei - ne Glöckchen klin - gen, dies wird dein Weibchen zu dir brin - gen!
3.G.
Then set the ma - gic bells a - ring - ing; 'Tis they thy sweetheart will be bring - ing.
So las - se dei - ne Glöckchen klin - gen, dies wird dein Weibchen zu dir brin - gen!
Pap.
me.
gehn.
f
PAPAGENO
How fool - ish of me to for - get them, how fool - ish of me to for -
Ich Narr ver - gass der Zau - ber - din - ge, ich Narr ver - gass der Zau - ber -
fp
f
fp

Pap.
-get them! At once a-jing-ling let.. me set them, That I my pret-ty maid may
-din-ge! Er-klin-ge, Glocken-spiel, er-klin-ge! Ich muss mein lie-bes Mäd-chen
f
p
Pap.
see, that I my pret-ty...maid may see.
sehn, ich muss mein lie-bes Mäd-chen sehn!
The GENII go out.
He plays on the bells.
Allegro
Bells
8
PAPAGENO
Ma-gic bells a-ring-ing, Find my sweet-heart's
Klin-get, Glöck-chen, klin-get! schafft mein Mäd-chen
Pap.
ear; Lure of laugh-ter fling-ing, Fetch my sweet-heart
her! Klin-get, Glöck-chen, klin-get! schafft mein Mäd-chen
tr

Pap.
here. Ma - gic bells a - ring-ing,
her! Klin-get, Glöck-chen, klin-get,
Pap.
Find my sweet-heart's ear;......Lure of laugh-ter fling - ing, Fetch my sweet - heart
schafft mein Mäd - chen her!......klin-get, Glöck-chen, klin - get, schafft mein Mäd - chen
Pap.
here. Lure of laugh-ter fling - ing, Fetch my sweet-heart here,
her! klin-get, Glöck-chen, klin - get, bringt mein Weib - chen her,
Bells
Pap.
fetch her here, yes, fetch her here, yes, fetch her
bringt sie her, mein Mäd - chen her, mein Weib - chen

The GENII return with PAPAGENA.
Exeunt.
1.G.
2.G.
Now turn a - bout and look this way!
Nun, Pa - pa - ge - no, sieh dich um!
3.G.
Now turn a - bout and look this way!
Nun, Pa - pa - ge - no, sieh dich um!
Pap.
here.
her!
cresc.
f
p
PAPAGENA
Pa - - pa - pa, Pa - -
Pa - - pa - pa, Pa - -
PAPAGENO
Pa - - pa - pa, Pa - pa - pa - pa,
Pa - - pa - pa, Pa - pa - pa - pa,
She
- pa - pa - pa, Pa-pa-pa - pa-pa-pa-pa - pa,
- pa - pa - pa, Pa-pa-pa - pa-pa-pa-pa - pa,
He
Pa-pa-pa - pa-pa-pa-pa - pa, Pa-pa-pa-pa-
Pa-pa-pa - pa-pa-pa-pa - pa, Pa-pa-pa-pa-

She
Pa-pa-pa-pa-pa, Pa-pa-pa-pa-pa-pa-pa-pa-ge - no!
Pa-pa-pa-pa - pa, Pa-pa-pa-pa-pa-pa-pa-pa-ge - no!
He
-pa, Pa-pa-pa-pa-pa-pa-pa-pa-ge - na! Caught at....
-pa, Pa-pa-pa-pa-pa-pa-pa-pa-ge - na! Bist du...
She
Yes, no more shall I re - fuse thee.
Nun bin ich dir ganz ge - ge - ben!
He
last, no more I lose thee! Thou'lt be.. mine to thy last
mir nun ganz ge - ge - ben? Nun, so... sei mein lie-bes
She
Yes, we'll share a cage to - ge - ther, a cage to - ge - ther, a cage to - ge-ther.
Nun, so... sei mein Herzens-täubchen, mein Herzens-täub-chen, mein Her-zens-täub-chen!
He
fea-ther? a cage to - ge - ther, a cage to - ge-ther.
Weib-chen! mein lie - bes Weib-chen, mein lie - bes Weib-chen!
cresc.
f
She
How de - light - ful it will
Wel - - che Freu - de wird das
He
How de - light-ful it will be,
Wel - - che Freu-de wird das sein,
p

She: be, / sein,

Now the time has come for pair-ing, When that
wenn die Göt-ter uns be-den-ken, uns-rer

He: Now the time has come for pair-ing,
wenn die Göt-ter uns be-den-ken,

When that
uns-rer

She: great-est joy we're shar-ing, when that great-est joy we're shar-ing, A nest of lit-tle birds to
Lie-be Kin-der schen-ken, uns-rer Lie-be Kin-der schen-ken, so lie-be klei-ne Kin-der-

He: great-est joy we're shar-ing, when that great-est joy we're shar-ing, A nest of lit-tle birds to
Lie-be Kin-der schen-ken, uns-rer Lie-be Kin-der schen-ken, so lie-be klei-ne Kin-der-

ritardando

She: see, lit-tle birds, lit-tle birds, lit-tle birds, a nest of
-lein, Kin-der-lein, Kin-der-lein, Kin-der-lein, so lie-be

He: see, lit-tle birds, lit-tle birds, lit-tle birds, a nest of
-lein, Kin-der-lein, **ritardando** Kin-der-lein, Kin-der-lein, so lie-be

in tempo

She: lit-tle birds to see, a nest of..... lit-tle birds to see.
klei-ne Kin-der-lein, so lie-be..... klei-ne Kin-der-lein!

He: lit-tle birds to see, a nest of..... lit-tle birds to see. First............
klei-ne Kin-der-lein, so lie-be..... klei-ne Kin-der-lein! Erst............

The Magic Flute

She
He
Next.................comes a lit-tle Pa-pa-ge - na,
Dann...............ei-ne klei-ne Pa-pa-ge - na,
........comes a lit-tle Pa-pa - ge - no,
.... ei-nen kleinen Pa-pa - ge - no,
Then.........
dann........
tr
f
p
Then...............comes an-o-ther Pa-pa - ge-na,
dann............... wie-der ei-ne Pa-pa-ge-na,
Pa-pa-
........comes an-o-ther Pa-pa - ge - no,
.... wie-der ei-nen Pa-pa-ge - no,
Pa-pa-ge-no,
-ge-na,
Pa-pa - ge-na, Pa-pa-ge-na, Pa-pa - ge - na!
-ge-na,
Pa-pa - ge-na, Pa-pa-ge-na, Pa-pa - - ge - - na!
Pa-pa-ge-no,
Pa-pa-ge-no, Pa-pa - ge - no!
Pa-pa-ge-no, Pa-pa - - ge - - no!
cresc.
fp
Oh where's the nest will e'er con-tain us,
Es ist das höch-s der Ge-füh-le,
With such a
wenn vie-le,
Oh where's the nest will e'er con-tain us,
Es ist das höch-ste der Ge-füh-le,

She
He
crowd .... of
vie - - - - - - - - - - - - - - - - - - le
With such a crowd of Pa-pa - ge-nos, Pa-pa-pa-pa-pa-pa - ge-nos, Pa-pa-pa-pa-pa-pa-
wenn vie - le Pa - pa-pa-pa - ge-no, Pa-pa-pa-pa-pa-pa - ge-no, Pa-pa-pa-pa-pa-pa-
mfp
Pa-pa-pa-pa-pa-pa-pa-pa-ge - nas As we shall some........ day hope to
Pa-pa-pa-pa-pa-pa-pa-pa-ge - na der El - tern Se - gen wer - den
-pa-pa-pa-pa-pa-pa-pa-pa-ge - nos As we shall some........ day hope to
-pa-pa-pa-pa-pa-pa-pa-pa-ge - no der El - tern Se - gen wer - den
p
f
see? Oh where's the nest will e'er con - tain us,
sein. Es ist das höch-ste der Ge - füh - le,
see? Oh where's the nest will e'er con - tain us, With such a
sein. Es ist das höch-ste der Ge - füh - le, wenn vie - le,
With such a crowd of Pa - pa - ge-nas, Pa-pa-pa-pa-pa-pa - ge-nas, Pa-pa-pa-pa-pa-pa-
wenn vie - le Pa - pa-pa-pa - ge-na, Pa-pa-pa-pa-pa-pa - ge-na, Pa-pa-pa-pa-pa-pa-
crowd .... of
vie - - - - - - - - - - - - - - - - - - le

She
-ge-nas, Pa-pa-pa-pa-pa-pa-pa-ge-nas As we shall some day hope to
-ge-na, Pa-pa-pa-pa-pa-pa-pa-ge-na der El-tern Se-gen wer-den
He
Pa-pa-pa-pa-pa-pa-pa-pa-pa-ge-nos As we shall some day hope to
Pa-pa-pa-pa-pa-pa-pa-pa-pa-ge-no der El-tern Se-gen wer-den
p
f
p
She
see? Pa-pa-ge-na, Pa-pa-ge-na, Pa-pa-pa-pa-pa-pa-pa-pa-pa-pa-
sein. Pa-pa-ge-na, Pa-pa-ge-na, Pa-pa-pa-pa-pa-pa-pa-pa-pa-pa-
He
see? Pa-pa-ge-no, Pa-pa-ge-no, Pa-pa-pa-pa-pa-pa-pa-pa-pa-pa-
sein. Pa-pa-ge-no, Pa-pa-ge-no, Pa-pa-pa-pa-pa-pa-pa-pa-pa-pa-
She
-ge-na, As we shall some day hope to see? Pa-pa-ge-na, Pa-pa-
-ge-na, der El-tern Se-gen wer-den sein, Pa-pa-ge-na Pa-pa-
He
-ge-no, As we shall some day hope to see? Pa-pa-ge-no, Pa-pa-
-ge-no, der El-tern Se-gen wer-den sein, Pa-pa-ge-no, Pa-pa-
cresc.
f
p
She
-ge-na, Pa-pa-pa-pa-pa-pa-pa-pa-pa-pa-ge-na, As we shall some day hope to
-ge-na, Pa-pa-pa-pa-pa-pa-pa-pa-pa-pa-ge-na, der El-tern Se-gen wer-den
He
-ge-no, Pa-pa-pa-pa-pa-pa-pa-pa-pa-pa-ge-no, As we shall some day hope to
-ge-no, Pa-pa-pa-pa-pa-pa-pa-pa-pa-pa-ge-no, der El-tern Se-gen wer-den
cresc.
f

She
see, as we shall someday hope to see, as we shall someday hope to see?
sein, der El-tern Se-gen wer-den sein, der El-tern Se-gen wer-den sein.
He
see, as we shall someday hope to see, as we shall someday hope to see?
sein, der El-tern Se-gen wer-den sein, der El-tern Se-gen wer-den sein.
p
f
p
She
Pa-pa-pa-pa-pa-pa-ge-na!
Pa-pa-pa-pa-pa-pa-ge-no!
Pa-pa-pa-pa-pa-pa-
Pa-pa-pa-pa-pa-pa-
He
Pa-pa-pa-pa-pa-pa-ge-no, Pa-pa-pa-pa-pa-pa-
Pa-pa-pa-pa-pa-pa-ge-no, Pa-pa-pa-pa-pa-pa-
f
She
-ge-na, Pa-pa-pa-pa-pa-pa-ge-na, Pa-pa-pa-pa-pa-pa-ge - - - na!
-ge-na, Pa-pa-pa-pa-pa-pa-ge-na, Pa-pa-pa-pa-pa-pa-ge - - - na!
He
-ge-no, Pa-pa-pa-pa-pa-pa-ge-no, Pa-pa-pa-pa-pa-pa-ge - - - no!
-ge-no, Pa-pa-pa-pa-pa-pa-ge-no, Pa-pa-pa-pa-pa-pa-ge - - - no!
Più moderato
p

Scene 10. **Before the temple. It is dark; MONOSTATOS enters stealthily, beckoning on the QUEEN OF NIGHT and the THREE LADIES.**

mf
p
MONOSTATOS
With si-lent foot-steps for-ward steal-ing, The tem-ple gates we soon shall
Nur stil-le, stil - le, stil - le, stil - le! Bald dringen wir in Tem - pel
QUEEN OF NIGHT
In darkness our ap-proach con-ceal-ing, We will our just re-venge ob - tain.
Nur stil-le, stil-le, stil - le, stil-le! Balddringenwir in Tem-pel ein.
THREE LADIES
In darkness our ap-proach con-ceal-ing, We will our just re-venge ob - tain.
Nur stil-le, stil-le, stil - le, stil-le! Balddringenwir in Tem-pel ein.
In darkness our ap-proach con-ceal-ing, We will our just re-venge ob - tain.
Nur stil-le, stil-le, stil - le, stil-le! Balddringenwir in Tem-pel ein.
M.
gain.
ein.
Re-
Doch
M.
- mem - ber, Queen, thy word, ful - fil it; Thy child Pa - mi - na must be
Für - stin, hal - te Wort! Er - fül - le: dein Kind muss mei - ne Gat - tin

QUEEN OF NIGHT
I gave my word; yes, thus I will it: My child Pa-mi-na shall be
Ich hal-te Wort; es ist mein Wil-le, mein Kind soll dei-ne Gat-tin
M.
mine.
sein.
Ped. *
Qu.
(Thunder)
thine, my child Pa-mi-na shall be thine.
sein, mein Kind soll dei-ne Gat-tin sein.
1st LADY
2nd LADY
Her child, her child, her child Pa-mi-na shall be thine.
3rd LADY
Ihr Kind, ihr Kind, ihr Kind soll dei-ne Gat-tin sein.
Yes, yes, her child Pa-mi-na, Pa-mi-na shall be thine.
Ihr Kind soll dei-ne Gat-tin, soll dei-ne Gat-tin sein.
MONOSTATOS
What is that noise of dis-tant rumb-ling, That in me wakes a name-less
Doch still, ich hö-re schrecklich Rau-schen wie Donner-ton und Was-ser-
mf
p
QUEEN OF NIGHT
Yes, hark! it fills the soul with tremb-ling, As if an earth-quake now drew
Ja, fürch-ter-lich ist die-ses Rau-schen, wie fernen Don-ners Wie-der-
THREE LADIES
Yes, hark! it fills the soul with tremb-ling, As if an earth-quake now drew
Ja, fürch-ter-lich ist die-ses Rau-schen, wie fernen Don-ners Wie-der-
Yes, hark! it fills the soul with tremb-ling, As if an earth-quake now drew
Ja, fürch-ter-lich ist die-ses Rau-schen, wie fernen Don-ners Wie-der-
M.
fear?
-fall.

Qu.
1. L.
2. L.
3. L.
M.
near.
-hall!
We'll fall up - -
Dort wol - len
All in the tem-ple are col - lect-ed.
Nunsindsie in des Tem-pels Hal-len.
We'll fall up -
Dort wollen
mf p
- on them un - sus-pect - ed, we'll fall up - on them un - sus -
wir sie ü - ber-fal - len, dort wol-len wir sie ü - ber -
We'll fall up - on them un-sus-pect - ed, we'll fall up - on them un-sus -
Dort wol-len wir sie ü - ber - fal - len, dort wol-len wir sie ü - ber -
We'll fall up - on them un - sus-pect - ed, un - sus -
Dort wol-len wir sie ü - ber - fal - len, ü - ber -
Ped.

Qu.
-pect-ed; We will des-troy that impious band With fire and sword throughout this
-fal-len, die Frömmler til-gen von der Erd' mit Feu-ers-glut und mächt-gem
1.L. 2.L.
-pect-ed; We will des-troy that im-pious band With fire and sword throughout this
-fal-len, die Frömmler til-gen von der Erd' mit Feu-ers-glut und mächt-gem
3.L.
-pect-ed; We will des-troy that im-pious band With fire and sword throughout this
-fal-len, die Frömmler til-gen von der Erd' mit Feu-ers-glut und mächt-gem
M.
-pect-ed; We will des-troy that im-pious band With fire and sword throughout this
-fal-len, die Frömmler til-gen von der Erd' mit Feu-ers-glut und mächt-gem
MONOSTATOS and the LADIES kneel before the QUEEN.
Qu.
land.
Schwert.
1.L. 2.L.
land. O star-ry Queen of ho-ly night, O star-ry
Schwert. Dir, gros-se Kö-ni-gin der Nacht, dir, gros-se
3.L.
land. O star-ry Queen of ho-ly night, O star-ry
Schwert. Dir, gros-se Kö-ni-gin der Nacht, dir, gros-se
M.
land. O star-ry Queen of ho-ly night, O star-ry
Schwert. Dir, gros-se Kö-ni-gin der Nacht, dir, gros-se
tr
mf p
1.L. 2.L.
Queen of ho-ly night, To thee al-le-giance true.... we
Kö-ni-gin der Nacht, sei uns-rer Ra-che Op-fer ge-
3.L.
Queen of ho-ly night, To thee al-le-giance true.... we
Kö-ni-gin der Nacht, sei uns-rer Ra-che Op-fer ge-
M.
Queen of ho-ly night, To thee al-le-giance true.... we
Kö-ni-gin der Nacht, sei uns-rer Ra-che Op-fer ge-
tr
mf p

Thunder. SARASTRO appears above.
QUEEN OF NIGHT
'Tis
Zer-
1. L.
2. L.
plight.
-bracht.
'Tis
Zer-
3. L.
plight.
-bracht.
'Tis
Zer-
M.
plight.
-bracht.
'Tis
Zer-
p
ff
Qu.
shat - ter'd and bro - ken for e - ver our pow'r; To dark - ness and
-schmet - tert, zer-nich - tet ist un - se - re Macht, wir al - le ge-
1. L.
2. L.
shat - ter'd and bro - ken for e - ver our pow'r; To dark - ness and
-schmet - tert, zer-nich - tet ist un - se - re Macht, wir al - le ge-
3. L.
shat - ter'd and bro - ken for e - ver our pow'r; To dark - ness and
-schmet - tert, zer-nich - tet ist un - se - re Macht, wir al - le ge-
M.
shat - ter'd and bro - ken for e - ver our pow'r; To dark - ness and
-schmet - tert, zer-nich - tet ist un - se - re Macht, wir al - le ge-

Qu.
death are we doom'd from this hour!
-stür - zet in e - - wi - ge Nacht!
1. L.
2. L.
death are we doom'd from this hour!
-stür - zet in e - - wi - ge Nacht!
3. L.
death are we doom'd from this hour!
-stür - zet in e - - wi - ge Nacht!
M.
death are we doom'd from this hour!
-stür - zet in e - - wi - ge Nacht!
The QUEEN, the LADIES and MONOSTATOS
disappear. TAMINO, PAMINA, the GENII, PRIESTS and People have followed SARASTRO on to the stage, which now
becomes light.
RECIT.
SARASTRO
The sun's gol-den ra-diance drives dark night a-
Die Strah-len der Son-ne ver-trei - ben die
Maestoso
Andante
S.
-way; The king-dom of er - ror to truth yields the day.
Nacht, zer-nich-ten der Heuchler er - schli - - che-ne Macht.

Soprano
Hail, ye souls en - light - en'd! Hail, ye souls en - light - en'd! once blind, now ye
Heil sei euch Ge - weih - ten! Heil sei euch Ge - weih - ten! Ihr dran-get durch
Contralto
Hail, ye souls en - light - en'd! Hail, ye souls en - light - en'd!
Heil sei euch Ge - weih - ten! Heil sei euch Ge - weih - ten!
Ch.
Tenor
Hail, ye souls en - light - en'd! Hail, ye souls en - light - en'd!
Heil sei euch Ge - weih - ten! Heil sei euch Ge - weih - ten!
Bass
Hail, ye souls en - light - en'd! Hail, ye souls en - light - en'd!
Heil sei euch Ge - weih - ten! Heil sei euch Ge - wei - ten!

see;.. Thanks, thanks,
Nacht.. Dank, Dank,
once blind, now ye see; Thanks, thanks,
Ihr dran - get durch Nacht. Dank, Dank,
Ch.
once blind, now ye see; Thanks, thanks,
Ihr dran - get durch Nacht. Dank, Dank,
once blind, now ye see; Thanks, thanks,
Ihr dran-get durch Nacht. Dank, Dank,

Ch.
thanks to great O - si - - ris! thanks, thanks, thanks,
Dank sei dir, O - si - - ris, Dank, Dank dir,
Allegro
I - - sis, to thee!
I - - sis, ge - - bracht!
I - sis, to thee!
I - sis, ge - - bracht!
Allegro

Ch.
p
f
Through dark - ness and er - ror they once sought their way; Vic -
Es sieg - te die Stär - ke und krö - net zum Lohn die
Through dark - ness and er - ror they once sought their way; Vic -
Es sieg - te die Stär - ke und krö - net zum Lohn die
Through dark - ness and er - ror they once sought their way; Vic -
Es sieg - te die Stär - ke und krö - net zum Lohn die
Through dark - ness and er - ror they once sought their way; Vic -
Es sieg - te die Stär - ke und krö - net zum Lohn die
- to - rious we hail them in tri - umph to - day.
Schön - heit und Weis - heit mit e - - wi - ger Kron'.
- to - rious we hail them in tri - umph to - day.
Schön - heit und Weis - heit mit e - - wi - ger Kron'.
- to - rious we hail them in tri - umph to - day.
Schön - heit und Weis - heit mit e - - wi - ger Kron'.
- to - rious we hail them in tri - umph to - day.
Schön - heit und Weis - heit mit e - - wi - ger Kron'.

Ch.
p
By Na - ture di - rec - ted, By
Es sieg - te die Stär - ke, es
cresc.
f
Rea - son pro - tec - ted, The high place of Wis - dom now have they found,.........
sieg - te die Stär - ke und krö - net zum Lohn, und krö - net zum Lohn...........

Ch.
Their faith - - ful... com - pan - - ion.. the...
die Schön - - heit und Weis - - heit mit...
Their faith-ful companion the
die Schön-heit und Weis-heit mit
Their faith-ful compan-ion
die Schön-heit und Weis-heit
Their faith-ful compan-ion
die Schön-heit und Weis-heit
flute's ma - - gic sound,............ Their faith - - ful... com - pan - - ion.. the...
e - wi - - ger Kron',............ die Schön - heit und Weis - - heit mit...
flute's ma - - gic sound,........... Their faith-ful compan-ion the
e - wi - - ger Kron',............ die Schönheit und Weis-heit mit
the flute's ma-gic sound,............ Their faith-ful com-pan-ion
mit e - wi-ger Kron',............ die Schön-heit und Weisheit
the flute's ma-gic sound,............ Their faith-ful com-pan-ion
mit e - wi-ger Kron',............ die Schön-heit und Weisheit

Ch.
flute's ma - - gic sound. 'Twas on - ly the voice of that mu - sic had
e - wi - - ger Kron'. Es sieg - te die Stär - ke und krö - net zum
flute's ma - - gic sound. 'Twas on - ly the voice of that mu - sic had
e - wi - - ger Kron'. Es sieg - te die Stär - ke und krö - net zum
the flute's ma-gic sound. 'Twas on - ly the voice of that mu - sic had
mit e - wi-ger Kron'. Es sieg - te die Stär - ke und krö - net zum
the flute's ma-gic sound. 'Twas on - ly the voice of that mu - sic had
mit e - wi-ger Kron'. Es sieg - te die Stär - ke und krö - net zum
might To guard them and guide them to Love and to Light, to
Lohn die Schön - heit und Weis - heit mit e - wi-ger Kron', mit
might To guard them and guide them to Love and to Light, to
Lohn die Schön - heit und Weis - heit mit e - wi-ger Kron', mit
might To guard them and guide them to Love and to Light, to
Lohn die Schön - heit und Weis - heit mit e - wi-ger Kron', mit
might To guard them and guide them to Love and to Light, to
Lohn die Schön - heit und Weis - heit mit e - wi-ger Kron', mit

Ch.
Love and to Light, to Love and to
e - - - wi - - ger Kron', mit e - - - wi - - ger
Light.
Kron'.
p
f